50

Healing
the Body Betrayed

A Self-Paced, Self-Help Guide

to Regaining Psychological

Control of Your Chronic Illness

Robert A. Klein, Ph.D.
Marcia Goodman Landau, Ph.D.

Healing the Body Betrayed: A Self-Paced, Self-Help Guide to
Regaining Psychological Control of Your Chronic Illness
©1992 by Robert A. Klein, Ph.D., and Marcia Goodman
Landau, Ph.D.

Library of Congress Cataloging-in-Publication Data

Klein, Robert, 1941-
     Healing the body betrayed: a self-paced, self-
     help guide to regaining psychological control of
     your chronic illness/Robert A. Klein,
     Marcia Goodman Landau.
          p. cm.
     Includes index
     ISBN 1-56561-003-2 (pbk.) $12.95
     1. Chronic diseases — Psychological aspects.
     I. Goodman Landau, Marcia.   II. Title
     RC108.K56   1992
     616'.001'9 — dc20   92-8387
                                   CIP

Edited by: Carol Danielson
Cover and Interior Design: Dan Norquist
Cover Photograph: Robert Randall
Printed in the United States of America

10 9 8 7 6 5 4 3 2 1

Published by:
DCI/CHRONIMED Publishing
P.O. Box 47945
Minneapolis, MN 55447-9727

The end of all our exploring
Will be to arrive where we started
And know the place for the first time
T. S. Eliot

Dedication

To my family—

Inspirational and supportive.
-M.G.L.

To:

My friend Robert Levy—for being there.

My wife Norma—for being there and here,
at all times and always.

My mother Jean Miller Klein—for imparting
to me her remarkable strength, perseverance,
and courage.

" . . . gratitude is the memory of the heart."
-R.A.K.

Table of Contents

Chronic illness is a lonely experience. It makes for a sense of uniqueness that often leads to a feeling of separateness and alienation. It tends to foster the perception that you are in a world of your own and cannot join the ranks of mainstream culture. Antidotes for this scenario are discussed.

Those with a chronic illness struggle because medical problems typically present themselves in overlapping or fluctuating cycles rather than as absent or present. The chronic sufferer is easily swayed, and fear of this suggestibility often interferes with daily activity. It helps to sort out the transient from the serious episodes. Learning to be realistically optimistic is a task that is difficult, but one that must be tackled.

Keeping track of your illness is a demanding, continuous— indeed chronic—task. But it must be done. This chapter shows you how and why.

Chronic illness presents new behavioral challenges, both un-wanted and unexpected. Change can be exhausting and prepa-ration may seem impossible. Daily life looms as insurmount-able. Others are not aware of the internal dialogue taking place. A practical worksheet is provided to help you identify, and respond to, the activities that elicit the mental struggles.

Sick people in our society are seen as faulty. To add to the burden, the mass media promote the non-necessity of suffering. Moreover, sickness elicits denial in our culture. As a result, chronic sufferers are doubly damned—feeling guilty from within and feeling misunderstood and criticized from outside. Fighting back, and how to handle the emotions from this "culture conflict" are focused upon in this chapter.

The person with a chronic illness has a saboteur around the corner. The urge to make big plans is natural, but retreat is often necessary. Short-term goals invite success. Fantasies and ex-cursions from reality can heal. Realistic goals can be alternated with the balm of imagination.

It is easy to stay with the familiar, especially when the vicissi-tudes of a chronic illness bring uncertainty on a regular basis. However, trying something new, making the uncomfortable comfortable, can be a healing and rewarding experience.

We all have our own private lists of experiences that renew and inspire us. We can order up a shot of inspiration in music, arts, sports, family life. We must seek out these "shots" aggressively and assertively. Context-setting is important. So is learning how to integrate inspiration into the daily routine.

The chronic sufferer must learn to cope with advice-givers and poultice-bearers. It helps to have in place an early-warning alert system designed to help you avoid too much advice that can ruin even the best of days. It is important to understand the ever-present vulnerability to advice and the accompanying longing for cures. Identifying people, places, and times that are intrusive can help you to avoid the next confrontation.

Physical stress will often decrease your ability to think and judge correctly, sometimes at a critical period. The more you hurt, the more you experience depression and anxiety, resulting in a lowered ability to think clearly and judge situations well. There are ways to acquire judgement.

For some, the energy required to control and monitor the illness is so great that there is little time for anything else. Without joy there is little reason or motivation to take on the challenges of life or the struggles with an illness. The chronic sufferer actively has to seek out experiences that evoke a smile, a giggle or a hearty laugh.

Children face chronic illness with both depression and anger. They also have a unique flexibility and sense of energetic hope that older folks do not have. Chronic illnesses in children very sharply intrude upon their natural growth stages and influence the behavioral expectations of peers and authority figures. Caregivers need to be aware of how children's growth patterns will be affected by their chronic problems.

A new diagnosis of chronic illness can have a range of emotional impact. The past becomes distorted and the future seems uncertain. The present is confused. It is important at this time to be calm and patient, and to learn what to expect so that you can be prepared for what is to come.

It is not always easy to tell family and friends how you are feeling, especially when you want to say you would rather be alone. There is nothing wrong, and there is a lot that's right, about saying, "Ouch," when it is time to let others know you are uncomfortable.

This chapter touches on a ticklish problem. It asks you to consider the question of how well you care for, protect, and nurture the people who care about you. Other chapters have examined ways to improve how you attend to yourself. Now it is time to look in a different direction. It is time to look around and see if you may be coping in a way that is hurting the ones you love, and how you might change that.

People with a chronic illness or disability have a trio of disturbing feelings lurking in the shadows of their emotional lives. Others may come and go, but these three are universal. Acknowledging their presence is helpful to all concerned.

Your body holds astounding gifts that provide you with many possibilities for all kinds of sensory experiences. When you have a chronic disability, you tend to think more negatively than positively. The body becomes associated with bad experiences. In actuality, the mind can shift in its focus.

This chapter deals with four major issues that directly concern your body. Each is crucial to good health and emotional well-being. They are important enough to be the core issue of several books, not just brief parts of a chapter. Because their psychological impact is great for those with a chronic illness, they need to at least be touched upon in this context.

The people we interviewed not only survived with wisdom and spirit, they went beyond survival to reach out in a variety of ways to help or connect with others. They gathered their remarkable strengths and rose above the illness. It's important to remember their successes.

Also by Robert A. Klein —

Wounded Men, Broken Promises: How the Veterans Administration Betrays Yesterday's Heroes

Acknowledgements

It is usual in a book of this kind for the authors to acknowledge their gratitude to those who gave of their time and personal commitment to make the end-product possible. Further, the point is often made that it is the "expert" who has learned more from the insights of those interviewed than the other way around.

The writing of this volume confirmed that experience for us. Generous in revealing their feelings, patient, and insightful, those interviewed imparted a wisdom and individualized expertise that only the person with first-hand experience can understand and communicate. Whatever the merit of this book, much of it must be attributed to the words we quote herein. Any deficiencies or errors, of course, remain our own.

As so often happens in our daily lives, circumstances emerged that enlarged on those truisms. Before receiving the galley proofs back from our editor at ChroniMed (the last step before binding), one of us (Robert Klein) gained added (and unexpected) insight into the reality of the chronically ill. Results of a recent angiogram confirmed the need for bypass surgery. Floored by this information, Marcia Landau, already a veteran of these matters, reminded her colleague of a certain book, soon to be published, that might be helpful.

"Read the chapter, 'If You Have Just Been Diagnosed,'" she advised. "There's a lot of wisdom in it." And so I did (re)read it. And I was struck, again—but now from the added vantage of a pilgrim in the uncharted territory of personal involvement—by the warmth and courage and understanding shown by those we interviewed. And although we have changed the names, but not the circumstances, of many of those to whom we spoke, it is to them that the applause and thanks should be directed.

In particular, we wish to reiterate our deep respect for Sandra McCollum and Karen Stone, who have taken the time to think through and put in writing—with wit, energy, and a refreshing and healthy in-your-face defiance—powerful messages to bolster the stamina of any one of us.

We also must thank our intrepid research assistant and consummate interviewer, Alice Powsner, R.N., for her dedicated thoroughness and personal and professional interest in helping us make this book both informative and readable. Dan Matthews, Ph.D., found time in his peripatetic schedule to read the manuscript and offer his usual reasoned and graceful criticism. And a sincere thanks to our agent, Susan Zilber, for shepherding this project from start to finish, with a practiced eye for minimizing the inevitable roadblocks.

To Scott Obenshain, M.D., we offer our appreciation for connecting us with Sandra McCollum in the first place, not to mention his friendship, good nature, and even more striking good will in spending countless Sunday mornings throughout the past sixteen years as Robert Klein's stalwart tennis partner. Scott, we both assume that's only the beginning.

—*R.A.K.*
—*M.G.L.*
Albuquerque, New Mexico
February 3, 1992

Introduction—
Don't Read Any Further
Until You Read This

This book is worthless to you unless you read it. Obvious, isn't it?

But what may not be so obvious is that all of us, in our daily lives, unconsciously trigger a mental mechanism that makes it easier for us to deal with the limitations of our bodies. It helps us deal with painful emotional uncertainties and the consequences of psychological loss. It makes everything seem to go more smoothly by encouraging us to ignore our problems, to psychologically look the other way. This mechanism is called denial.

Because denial is not a conscious act, we are not aware that it is operating. Its psychological purpose is to reduce our anxiety and stress by dismissing or misrepresenting, often to ourselves, actual, painful situations. Denial rids us of anguish by making its sources seem to evaporate, by declaring they do not exist.

Denial is powerful and universal. It will make you not want to read this book. Denial will provide you with excuses to skip over a particularly pertinent chapter, or to put the book out of sight on a shelf. "I'll read it later when I really need it," is a good example of denial. And then you might add, "I'm not really that sick, anyway."

Maybe you're not. But the discomfort you feel when faced with unpalatable circumstances must be recognized.

Sometimes denial is an appropriate mechanism that helps us to live our lives with as little stress as possible. But often denial can be counterproductive; indeed, it *will* be counterproductive.

Ignoring problems, delaying their solutions, or making excuses may make you feel better for the moment. But things won't be made easier for you or your family. So be prepared. The material in this book will stimulate denial. In fact, the book is activating denial as you read this. Denial can harm you. So you are forewarned.

Reading this book is like getting an inoculation: When you are inoculated against a disease, you receive some of the very toxins that cause the disease. So it is with this book. Absorbing the information in this volume will help inoculate you against denial.

We make no guarantees. But we think it is critical for you to know from the beginning that denial packs a powerful wallop. Whatever your chronic illness, denial impedes your growth and stymies your progress. Acknowledge its masking power, and you can benefit from the following pages. Recognize the purpose of denial, and the recognition will set you free.

Now read the book.

Why This Book is Different

Healing the Body Betrayed is a coping manual for a wide array of physical problems. It is designed for people who have recently been diagnosed and for those who have been ill for some time, and for the families of both.

Books of this type are usually written for someone with a specific illness or disability, such as diabetes, AIDS, asthma, arthritis, lupus, cancer or paraplegia. Why, then, should *you* read this book?

Because it's different. It considers the impact of many kinds of physical problems, all under one cover. It deals with the psyche—what goes on in your head.

Doctors, psychologists, psychiatrists, shamans, curanderos and all kinds of counselors have known for years that there are basic similarities in the mental coping processes for widely different problems. In fact, if you talk with a range of people—your barber or hairdresser, bartender, job supervisor, clergyman, tailor—all probably know this truth, at least on some level.

All people who have recently come to grips with disability or illness share the knowledge that something important in their lives has changed. They have learned, or are learning, that they can no longer take good health for granted. They need to make new adjustments. They all know privately that their lives are now different. Most struggle quietly—or not so quietly—with this fact.

"Sometimes I get very angry," says Dorothy McCormick, who has multiple sclerosis. "I say 'fuck' a lot. I sit and watch people walking. I know walking is easy. I used to do that."

Each illness has its own coping consequences and each person adjusts in his or her own way. But there are common reactions. These include varying degrees of irritability, anger, despair, depression, anxiety, ambivalence, amazement, and problems with intimacy. These may be followed by acceptance, creative problem-solving, and a renewed sense of challenge. Each of the many tasks required to adjust elicits a commonality of coping skills of different speeds and styles. There is no predicting exactly how the process will go, but a long-standing body of information tells us what to expect.

No Guidelines

There are no pat answers, no classes or guidebooks, no lectures that offer a complete solution to your struggle with your loss of physical prowess. Without help or guidance, you may experience potent daily frustration with the differences between your previous, healthy self and your current, changed self. As with the death of a loved one, people with a disability or chronic illness grieve the passing of their former selves.

Still, all is not hopeless. Often right next door, down the street, or a telephone call away, someone is struggling with a physical problem and having similar reactions. Ironically, if you meet, talk, or pass each other at the corner, the gas station, the supermarket, golf course, or at church, you do not discuss how you really feel. The secret mission of adjustment and adaptation does not lie in the socially polite, "How're you doin'?" script.

Rebecca Steinberg was diagnosed with breast cancer in 1972. She says, "Networking with other people who haven't been where I've been yet and, and to whom I feel I have something to offer—that's what's rewarding to me and rewarding to them. Because, unless you've been there, you simply can't understand what it feels like." Rebecca hopes she may inspire others by her example. "'Hey, if she can do it, maybe I can too'."

Through the words and experiences of people we have interviewed, we tell you what the common unspoken problems are among those with chronic physical problems. And we tell you how others, in similar circumstances, regardless of their disability, manage their lives and their emotions.

Some of the examples in this book are contradictory. But that's the point: There is no one way to react, respond, or cope with chronic illness. We are not advocating any particular method of dealing with the issues facing you. This book presents a range of possibilities. You choose or create what's comfortable for you. In these pages you will find concrete, specific suggestions as well as personal, philosophical overviews. We expect the mix will prove to be stimulating.

As you read through the chapters you also will note an alternating rhythm between two different messages. One message says pay attention to your body, know what is happening, take care of yourself. In contrast, another message invites you to step away from your internal concerns and move into the world around you, become involved with people, ideas, and things.

The struggles is between paying attention to personal needs and learning to reach out to others. It is a rhythm, or tension, that is part of the human condition, and chronic illness makes it especially intense. Both messages, seemingly contradictory, have a place in your life.

In addition, you will probably feel that some of the factual material, personal stories, and chapter exercises are not useful or pertinent to you. That may be true *now*. But, as you probably have already realized, circumstances and perspectives change over time. Don't be surprised if you come back to material you dismissed earlier, only to find it relevant and right for you at a later point in your coping process.

As Susan Abeyta, who recently had a mastectomy, puts it: "There's no right way to do this, there's no wrong way to do this. There's only your way. And by definition, your way is the right way. You're the one doing it."

Childhood Memories

This book has another unique aspect. It looks at the way physical disabilities evoke defenses or old childhood fears. It is important to remember that this is not the first time you have faced uneven odds in life. This is not the first time you wondered whether you could keep up. Nor is this the first time you've been surrounded by others who were stronger and seemed more competent than you. You experienced all of these in childhood.

A 2-year-old watches big sister easily turn on the T.V. set or make a sandwich. A 5-year-old looks on with awe at the teenager next-door who glides gracefully down the street on a bicycle. The junior high school girl gazes longingly at the high school sophomore who dresses stylishly and seems at ease with her peers.

Interestingly, physical problems of adulthood can bring back some painful and frustrating childhood memories. All of us can recall feeling alone, less competent, different, and powerless. Chronic illness and disability can be threats to adult independence. They may also undermine the skills acquired so slowly and painstakingly throughout childhood, thereby undermining the sense of self we have come to take for granted.

These emotions do not differentiate among the various chronic illnesses or physical disabilities. All are part of the struggle to gain control. Who are the people confronting the limitations their illness or disability places on them?

- The arthritic patient who cannot zip up a zipper to go out for a job interview.

- The diabetic planning a vacation who must take care to check sugar levels and prepare for possible emergencies before walking out the door.

- The asthmatic who must tune in carefully to her breathing as she climbs the steps of the neighborhood library.

- The cancer patient who must always remain hypervigilant to changes in the body, and for whom regular checkups with the doctor never cease.

- The paraplegic in the wheelchair who must assess the size of the doorway of his friend's new home before visiting.

- The woman with lupus who guards carefully against the effects of bright sunlight at the family picnic.

- The heart patient for whom diet and exercise become daily survival rituals.

It seems like cod liver oil all over again, only this time it's not your mother handing out the dose—it's your illness.

The adult with a physical problem must go through tedious tasks associated with childhood, just as each child on the playground faces peers with self-consciousness, or perhaps fear, when trying out a new activity or game. No one wants to look foolish or feel clumsy. Adults, like children, need to figure out when to try new tasks and when to retreat. This trial-and-error approach is tough work, both physically and psychologically. Each person with a physical problem has to experiment with new strategies so as not to sabotage the necessary emotional adjustments.

Self-Sabotage

Adults may defy stress or respond to it erratically. One person pushes too hard, perhaps to exhaustion (like the youngster who won't get out of the pool). An adult with a physical problem may likewise retreat to passively watching television for hours and feeling emotionally paralyzed (not unlike the child who withdraws from more active peers and spends hours in her room staring at the walls, feeling alone and immobilized).

Children struggling with issues of competition may be angry and volatile, displaying tantrums and directing fury toward parents and friends. An adult with a physical problem may be angry all the time, perhaps even without knowing it, alienating old friends and placing family in a state of slow burn.

These are basic and common reactions described by people who have physical problems. There is no need to feel ashamed of these feelings. But there is a need to acknowledge our return to childhood behavior (psychologists call it *regression*), master the feelings, and move on.

This is not an easy thing to do. The person with a physical disability gets a raw deal—too little, too soon. We all know that, as we age, we lose some of our physical options. But a chronic illness or disability is an early rip-off regardless of the impairment or degree of adjustment necessary. Still, it is possible to figure out if you are doing all you can to get the most out of your life with your particular physical problem.

Dorothy McCormick, a corporate administrator, says, "If you lack self-confidence, it shows. People won't overextend themselves to help. Warmth begets warmth.

"People with a disability have a great deal of control over how others will respond. There are a few obstacles, but no high fences that can't be jumped. You have these limitations, but you can minimize the impact of the limitations, thereby minimizing the frustrations."

Following the guidelines in *Healing the Body Be-*

trayed will enable you to benefit from the extensive work of established psychological researchers, individuals who over the past 50 years have helped us to better understand the emotional workings of adults and children. The book incorporates the ideas of Anna Freud, Leopold Bellak, Aaron Beck, Abraham Maslow, Jean Piaget, and others and explains how *not* to fall back into dysfunctional childhood patterns.

Format

We have tried to make the book as clear and informative as possible. Each chapter begins with a quote and a short summary, and each chapter is independent of the others. You can pick and choose to read those chapters that are most pertinent or useful to you at the moment. All chapters end with a pencil-and-paper exercise specially devised to enable you to consolidate and follow through on the material covered in the chapter.

Don't expect to digest all you read at once, or even over a period of months or years. In fact, we suggest that you first read the chapter summaries and then skim over the pages, perhaps with the assistance of a family member or your doctor, before deciding how to proceed. While this book is yours, and the problems addressed are yours to solve, we also have intended it to be read and used by family members, friends and medical allies.

Finally, *Healing the Body Betrayed* contains good news and bad news. The good news is that you are not alone in your struggle with physical problems. There are many others out there like you—perhaps more than you have imagined.

The bad news is that you will have to do most of the work. This means, for example, noting changes in physical functioning and monitoring your less effective behavior styles by yourself. For some, doing these tasks will even become part of your daily routine.

"I can't chop up food anymore," Dorothy McCormick has come to realize. "I can't button buttons anymore. I have a difficult time tying my shoes. It's hard for me to put one foot in front of the other—which might or might not happen.

"But every morning, you get up and look in the mirror. It's like an affirmation. Put a smile on your face and say, 'Okay, it's time to go to work.' You have to do that."

Dorothy pauses briefly, then says: "People don't want to be around people who are miserable. I know I don't want to be around people who are miserable."

In the end, you are the one who can make a difference. This book offers guidance. Your curiosity, caring, motivation, discipline, flexibility, and courage will fill in the particulars.

Good luck.

1. My Body, My Car —
Marcia Landau's True Allegory

My own struggles with asthma have persisted for more than 25 years. After all that time, I can no longer distinguish between the illness's intrusion on my mental and emotional life space and the life space itself.

The intrusion is not dramatic and explosive. Quite the contrary. It just sort of creeps along, a tedious, insidious, subtle—in short, chronic—drain. Asthma has become a part of me; it is me, a much as my hands or my eyes or the professional work I do in my office. It is as much a piece of who I am as are the chores I do as a parent at home. It is always there, somewhere.

Sometimes life plays tricks on us. A small event, an inconsequential incident evokes a trail of mental associations that are powerful and compelling. As fate would have it, the preparation of this manuscript has put me through an ordinary experience that intertwines the reality of my illness with the everydayness of an activity we take for granted—in this case, a car ride.

Trying to explain the impact of a chronic illness to others, making them understand exactly what it is like, has always been hard for me. The story of my sputtering, ailing car, once so strong and predictable, is meant to illustrate my difficulties.

On a cold November evening, I had to drive from my office to the home of a terminally ill woman whom I was interviewing for this book. The initial interview session had been intense and was shortened by her weakness and fatigue. She feared that she had little time left to live. We scheduled a quick follow-up meeting so that her story would be complete.

Autumn nights in Albuquerque can be cold, with temperatures often in the teens, and this was an especially bitter evening. I was uncertain that my 13-year-old Oldsmobile would be up to the task.

In earlier days my car was pretty jazzy. It had a V-8 engine and a rather dazzling but subtle green coat. The upholstery was smooth tan leather and the car seemed to be all that I could wish for when I bought it.

It had pulled a trailer, traveled around the United States, and carried my kids to ice-skating, soccer games, and band practice. It was considered "my" car over the years and contains a wonderful Blaupunkt radio and tape deck installed by my family as a holiday gift.

On this particular evening, the old Olds was not in good shape. Six years ago its once-powerful motor had been replaced with a rebuilt engine. Now that engine was tired and functioning poorly. I had repeatedly brought the car in to be repaired and my usually optimistic mechanic, Danny, had been trying to tell me it was time to let it go.

Work on the inside of the engine would not pay, he said—I should start looking for another car. I resisted. Maybe it would last a few months more, I thought. Maybe 13 years was an unlucky time to make a switch. Maybe if I held on to it another six months, it might recover. (It didn't occur to me until later that I was using the defense of denial, so common in the aggravation of chronic illness problems.)

So, having just been checked and adjusted for the fourth time in one month, my car awaited me outside the

2

office. It was 6:30 P.M., and the night was clear and cold. I climbed into the front seat and started the engine.

It stalled.

The car had recently developed this annoying symptom. I panicked mildly. I talked to myself and pleaded with the unresponsive tons of steel. (I often speak to cars, elevators and traffic lights—not always good naturedly—when no one is around.) Finally, I coaxed it into moving out of the empty parking lot.

I tried to get up some speed as I turned onto the street, but there was no surge of energy when I pressed down on the accelerator. My car was behaving more and more like my lungs do during an asthma episode. Driving, like breathing when asthmatic, required careful planning for the next 45 minutes. I slowly cruised to the corner and began to anticipate the first of many stop signs. Potential disaster lay ahead.

A full stop meant the likelihood of a full stall. The car crawled to the stop sign, but I didn't completely halt. I figured if I slowed down from five miles per hour to two miles per hour, without stalling, I might not have to stop at the red light ahead of me. My heart beat a little faster as I approached the corner. I made it and turned right onto another major street.

As I passed each hurdle, I felt that all might be well if I found my ideal pace. But a new problem was rapidly emerging. Traffic was moving at a stupendous rate. I pushed on the pedal and got the car up to its full glorious potential of 15 miles per hour. The drivers around me were getting irritated. This was no time to be self-conscious as I had to prepare for the next light. My job was again to slow down before the light so as not to stop, stall, and get stuck. I made it, with leeway of one or two seconds.

I was becoming increasingly sensitive to the cold. My fingers were beginning to feel numb. I turned on the heater and the car went into spasms of sluggishness. I quickly shut it off and gripped the steering wheel.

We had miles to go and I was suddenly aware that they were all uphill. I was driving toward the base of the mountain and we had a climb ahead of us. I tried to look casual as my knuckles turned white on the wheel. My elbow rested awkwardly on the arm rest that had broken last month. My unwillingness to fix the arm rest was probably the first real clue that some part of me had become resigned to the car's demise. Breathing a little rapidly, I remembered first realizing years ago that my own body was failing me earlier than it should have been.

I turned on the radio, but it distracted me. The music that normally energized or relaxed and soothed was now abrasive and confusing noise. I shut it off, irritated.

I kept driving. At one point, the Olds lurched into a mighty sprint and the speedometer read a whopping 25 m.p.h. I thought to myself, "Ah, finally. You're back to normal and we're okay." Like those self-deceiving but expectant moments, days or weeks of serenity when my lungs released their constricting grip, I confidently looked at the drivers around me, feeling totally in charge. Life would be fine, even predictable, again.

The next traffic light proved my confidence to be premature. The car started to stall and I immediately shifted to neutral with one foot on the brake (we were going uphill) and one on the gas pedal.

The light changed and I shifted to drive. Cars were again honking and passing me. A police car went by, with the officer giving me a glaring stare.

I was beginning to grasp that this had been a terrible mistake. Maybe I should stop and call to cancel the appointment. Of course, if I stopped, I might not start again. I might have to call AAA to get home. Worse, my subject might not be available ever again.

I kept moving closer to the base of the mountain. The experience was unreal and was made more bizarre by the beauty of the crisp dry Albuquerque night. The combination of the darkness, the mountain ahead, and the sparkling lights in the clear air made this the kind of nighttime scene that draws travelers to New Mexico. The brief moment of reverie, taking me away from the immediate discomfort, was refreshing. But I was getting tired. My fingers seemed barely alive and my anxiety level was increasing.

The next 30 minutes were tortuous. I drove, shifted, raced the engine, and lurched in a four-wheel dance of unpredictable rhythm. In one horrible moment, as I navigated a wide intersection, the car stalled. Horns around me blasted. I stopped six lanes of traffic and sat helplessly, waiting to be accidentally hit. After two or three minutes, the car started.

As I approached the turnoff to my destination, my flexibility and coping style were forced to evolve to a greater level of complexity. I now had to (1) read the street signs, (2) slow down, (3) get past the residential stop signs, and (4) turn several times to zero in on my goal.

At one intersection, my timing was off. I approached the stop sign as usual, but I didn't count on another car coming through. We almost collided and then barely passed each other. Obscenities were hurled through the semi-darkness. I was confused and scared.

At last I found the house; now I was faced with another dilemma (as a veteran chronic illness sufferer, I was not surprised): finding a parking space and risking driving in reverse, a totally unknown tactic for my clunker in its current state. Together, we managed.

Throughout the trip, I had spoken to the car. I yelled, pleaded, begged, commended and cursed as we moved across the city. I even sang and hollered in some desperate moments. The amount of fear and tension I experienced was obvious only after I shut off the engine, this time by choice. I sat there somewhat stunned, and collapsed. It took time to turn to the role of researcher and interviewer and to reclaim my clinical skills.

The trip had been a painful reminder of an analogous experience I know only too well. Moving about when struggling with asthma when it feels ponderous and intrusive, my shell and facade outwardly presentable, others would never guess ("Dr. Landau, you look nice today"). But I always knew when the internal system was not working well.

At those times, a trip to the office, the store, or a movie seemed as difficult as climbing Mt. Everest. My body would chug along at a very slow pace but would fool me at times with a rush of adrenalin. I would frequently read the cues incorrectly and overdo my plans and daily goals.

Like my unpredictable automobile, I would find myself in situations that were too much for me. I would have to make decisions repeatedly about whether to go on or to stop and about whether to reveal my flaws or cover them up.

I would try to anticipate each rough spot, but I often miscalculated. There I would be, teaching a class or talking at a meeting, with little air available in the system. The asthma has been both a constant reminder of the limitations of my body and the strengths that often sustain me.

Like the car and the trip, my body and my illness are filled with messages. Some are subtle, some are direct. Some, paradoxically, like the effects of the disease itself, are both. Listen to them, and see how they fit.

There is a sense of compelling motivation to complete tasks when you feel your body's weakness. There may not be enough time or energy later.

Often, just to spite the illness, I take on impossible tasks to test my fortitude, to beat the odds. Always a rather bittersweet memory tugs at me, recalling and idealizing my health and attractiveness in earlier years. This somewhat distorted picture rises and elicits old longings.

I look at myself historically as strong, helpful, useful, and energetic. This image—or half-truth—motivates me; it keeps me going.

There is a repetitive pattern of ignoring sound advice about physical states. I have cast away many warnings. Sometimes it works, and I recover. Often, I am sicker than I realize.

Magical thinking, a close cousin to denial, perhaps even a sibling, dominates many rough physical periods: If I go three more days with no trouble, I'll be okay this summer. Or, all I need is one more day of good weather.

Perhaps I should not have pushed my car that night. Perhaps I should not have pushed my body on many occasions. Stretching limits is scary, but a little heroic. Risk-taking is necessary for a full life, but there is a fine line between excitement and terror.

The asthma has given me an existential view of every year and every day—even every hour. It has kept me humble and in constant awe of my body since I was 25, when it first began. It has kept me from some fun and frolic, but it also has taught me about my strengths and creativity. And it has made me understand much more about people's struggles and losses.

I would be delighted to get rid of the asthma any day, any time. But as long as it's here, it provides me with a daily challenging trip just as my car did on one cold night in November.

2. Illness Alienates

> We dance around in a
> ring and suppose,
> But the Secret sits in the
> middle and knows.
>
> **Robert Frost**

Chronic illness is a lonely experience. It makes for a sense of uniqueness that often leads to a feeling of separateness and alienation. It tends to foster the perception that you are in a world of your own and cannot join the ranks of mainstream culture. Antidotes for this scenario are discussed.

Sandra McCollum, 46, has had a severe pulmonary disease and an immune system disorder since the age of 2.

"For many years I did not want to talk to others about my illness; from the time I was in grade school I learned that a cough made a difference. Not only do I have a disease, but this disease also comes complete with its own sound effects.

"I wanted to be like everyone else, so I denied that I was unusual. I tried to do everything to prove that I was 'normal.' As long as I refused to accept my limitations, maybe I wouldn't have any.

"Gradually, I learned to accept my dreams with certain modifications (the nebulizer tucked away in my gym shorts, the portable Bennett machine perched in my dorm room that helped me get through college and graduate school). But I have never stopped dreaming those dreams, and still only reluctantly arbitrate the outcome so long as I don't have to relinquish complete control or negotiate away too much of the enjoyment."

People with chronic body problems are a minority. A de facto gulf exists between the person with a chronic illness and the population at large. The experiences of those we interviewed for this book confirm that perception. Many subtle hints remind them each day that they are left out, that they don't belong. The net result is a level of alienation that is ubiquitous if not universal.

Other cues are not so subtle. Messages of vim and vigor saturate the media and our consciousness. They place a burden upon those who fail to live up to the standards set by the healthy, the physically well off, and which are promoted by a huge array of purveyors of speed, perfection, and eternal youth. There is definitely nothing wrong with striving to meet challenging goals. The difficulty arises with the implication that those who do not, or cannot, are somehow not worthy of attention. Or when alternatives simply do not exist because of the physical limitations imposed by the illness.

The people we interviewed reported a variety of activities they cannot participate in because of these limitations. Down the block a family leaves for a movie or ball game. On the job, a group is getting ready to go out dancing after work. In the lunchroom, a huddle of men is planning a touch football tournament. The person with chronic illness feels left out, on the outside, as an observer watching, not as a participant.

A feeling of being different gets a toehold...and hangs on. The world appears to move by quickly. Sometimes, the chronically ill report they are clearly ignored and their problems cruelly disregarded. They feel forgotten and lost.

Healing the Body Betrayed offers thoughts and ideas we gathered from excellent "copers." But it is important to note that the woman who has had a mastectomy, the man with a heart condition, the grandfather with exhausting emphysema, the mother with painful arthritis, the teenager with asthma, all feel at times like second-class citizens.

There are activist groups trying to ensure equal rights for those with disabilities. Their existence alone serves to affirm that this culture often does not voluntarily respond to the needs of people with different problems. The feeling of alienation experienced by the disabled does not merely reflect distortions in their thinking. Although it may be viewed as a backhanded compliment, there can be some comfort in that validation.

A feeling of alienation sometimes revolves around friends and family. Those with a chronic disability often do not feel they are a useful and contributing part of the close groups to which they belong. At a picnic, for example, the chronically ill individual may silently wonder, "I can't participate in the usual volleyball game—will I mess it up for everyone?" "What if the meal contains salt or fat that is not on my diet? Should I tell anyone, or just eat and pretend to fit in?" "What if people think I move too slowly?" "Is my wheelchair going to make everyone uptight?"

Sometimes, you feel like a burden even in your own home. The disabled person may worry about sharing an equal load in the running of the household, perhaps even trying to do more than the others to compensate. They may feel upset that their presence adds extra expense and takes up extra time.

Finally, but importantly, those with chronic illness feel alienated from themselves. In their minds, they carry the vivid memory of a formerly healthy person. That person was someone they used to be or hoped to become. It did not work out that way.

Where is that person now? Where is that longed-for role they coveted and into which they hoped to evolve? That self is from the past and may not ever be a reality. The chronically ill person pines and grieves for that lost person. Whenever we spend time longing or mourning, we are not totally attuned to the present. That means our thoughts and feelings become separated. The result is further alienation.

Alienation begets alienation. The more out of touch we feel, the harder it is to feel relaxed and comfortable and the easier it is to feel removed and alienated. Instead of bouncing into life situations with vital energy and passion, people with chronic illnesses hold back.

They find ways to withdraw or emotionally hide. Sometimes they find ways to hide the symptoms. This "success" makes it even more tempting to maintain a "cover." Shortness of breath may be masked by moving about, rustling papers, or noisily washing dishes. Disturbing chest pains can be covered with a big smile. Joint pains are numbed by crossed legs and a tense posture.

Susan Abeyta's dilemma illustrates this problem. In February 1989, Susan had a bilateral mastectomy. Although she resumed her routine and maintained a network of friends after the operation, lingering questions remained in her mind about how others unfamiliar with her status perceived her. How should she proceed?

"That was something I had to figure out," Susan, 46, recalls. "And how I figured it out was I just had to bring myself to ask people. Well, it's hard to find a group of people to whom you can say, 'Do you notice something funny about me?' Everyone who knew me, knew—so you can't ask them.

"So you have to find a group of strangers who have spent enough time in your company that if it was something people noticed—whether you had breasts or not— they would have noticed, and yet don't know you well enough to know your history, but who you know well enough to ask them if they noticed."

At that time, Susan had been attending a group counseling class at a local university. "At the very end [of the semester], I said, 'I need to ask you all a question. Have you noticed . . . ?' Nobody noticed."

"Before," she says, "it was like a family secret. I'm living my whole life with this family secret. That was so much of who I was. I really couldn't connect with people because there was this secret that was really integral to who I am today. If I can't talk about that, then who I am or what I'm doing makes no sense at all."

The impracticality of the charade became evident.

"If you have a secret, then you can't call from work to make doctors' appointments. If the doctor calls and leaves a message, the secret's out of the bag. Pretty much now everyone knows—you can rely on the grapevine."

In the end, Susan became relaxed about telling others. "I just waited for an opening...," she says.

Alienation also alters the sense of what life will be like down the road. Others are talking about upcoming events. These may include dinners, vacation plans, a night at the movies—or something further along, like retirement. The person with a chronic illness has difficulty shifting from the present to the future. Why? Because the present weighs heavily on the body, and day-by-day coping takes a lot of energy. The result is alienation from a sense of one's future self.

Reactions to the cycles of illness all lead to estrangement and moodiness, a feeling of isolation, of loneliness. Unfortunately, this makes sense. We usually react to frustration with anger. So the person with the chronic problem has much to be irritated with and frustrated about every day.

People struggling with chronic illness experience secrets, shame, and low self-esteem.

Secrets take root because they serve well the chronically ill person's need to keep problems from others. A secret is a technique we learn in childhood to protect us from the intrusion of parents, siblings, and those with whom we do not want to share. Secrets have emotional power, but they also foster loneliness and separateness.

Because physical symptoms are often invisible, and because only you are immediately aware of them, they remain private experiences, or secrets. They are your personal cues to what is happening internally. They trigger actions, or inactions, on your part that others may not understand because they can't see the reasons for your behavior.

As a result, hiding internal, personal experiences

can alienate you from the external, interpersonal experiences of daily living. When we don't acknowledge or respond to our feelings, our closeness to other human beings is impaired, and our capacity for survival is restricted.

Sandra McCollum, a program director at a state medical school, had the opportunity to explain this.

"I talk to the third-year medical students and I say, 'Maybe you don't know what it's like to stay up all night not breathing.' But everybody has tried to function normally when it has seemed impossible for some reason. When that happens, fatigue, disappointment, or discouragement sets in. I think those are the feelings, maybe, that bind us together but the illness separates us from. But we all have a certain range of human experiences, and that's what we need to tap into."

Shame emerges when we feel our bodies are faulty, broken, and malfunctioning. You feel a little like you did when you were a child caught stealing a cookie or soiling your pants. You feel embarrassed. Shame is a universal experience. Think of Adam and Eve upon their expulsion from Eden.

Sandra McCollum observes: "I used to feel so isolated because I thought, 'Where do you go for a support group for somebody who's been on a ventilator 17 times...?' Then, what I really began to realize is that people didn't have to be on a ventilator that many times or even have a respiratory disease. There was something in everybody's life that they felt they must keep secret or they wouldn't be accepted."

The person with a chronic illness is at high risk for

making frequent mental comparisons to everyone around and coming out on the short end. The chronically ill person feels inappropriately "less" in all areas than do others: less attractive, less capable, less in control, and less powerful. The result is lowered self-esteem.

These are reflections of the alienation process. They were reported to a greater or lesser degree by all those we interviewed. Some however, learned at an early age, from an important figure, that disabilities are acceptable and that they should take pride in all aspects of who they are. They identified themselves as winners, as courageous people with persistence, brains, and creativity. The majority, though, has not been so fortunate. They experienced physical problems as a fall from wellness, and they had to do a great deal of work to re-establish good self-esteem.

Strategies in the healing process are multiple. As these steadfast people broke through their internal struggles, three steps seem apparent: self-awareness, grieving and sharing.

Self-awareness means the undoing of denial. It ratifies the person's acceptance of the physical condition and the taking on of the challenges it presents.

John Flanagan, 51, a disabled skier, swimmer and scuba-diving enthusiast, recalls the excitement he felt eight or nine years ago when he attended for the first time a national skiing event at which others with physical disabilities participated. Experiencing the variety of skiers with their variety of disabilities, he says, would have been very helpful to him when he was younger. To have had the experience of not feeling conspicuous because the people are either like you or different in a similar way, would have mattered then.

"For me, that was a final acceptance, or the beginning of a new phase of acceptance, and maybe even a bit of a period of mourning," John says, referring to the left leg he lost at age 18 in a heavy-equipment accident. It was an acceptance of a self-awareness, he adds, that said, "Hey, you are disabled. You are like these other people. It seemed like a new feeling of freedom, maybe from the denial."

Grieving involves the bittersweet farewell to old dreams that, although once wonderful, now have the power to entrap the ill person in the past rather than allow a release to the present and future.

Karen Stone can no longer trek through the wilderness. She has multiple sclerosis.

"I guess I have some adjusting to do," observes Karen. "Like being able to look at my hiking boots and say, 'Some wonderful times have been shared,' with a smile on my face and in my heart."

Sharing supposes reaching out and making external and public the problems that are going on (see Chapter 17). JoAnne Ricardo, diagnosed with scoliosis, cancer and diabetes, has an arresting perspective.

"I have had depression about isolation and loneliness, not about my body. I was in a serious depression after my mastectomy. People didn't want a lot to do with me."

JoAnne, 70, adds, "Your body is not the biggest problem in your life. Relationships, communality, and values are more important. Number one is 'mattering.' I am extremely engaged in the 'human family.' I talk about what's on my mind. I have friends, rich correspondences, and telephone calls. My money goes to Sprint."

Alienation is the curse of the chronically ill and the culture we live in does not help. People who are not disabled are not aware of the disabled person's problems. The solution is to recognize and truly confront the dilemma.

The potency and significance of alienation are yet more poignant, touching the universal, lonely depth of our own mortality. Sandra McCollum thinks the skills to articulate the feelings of loneliness and separateness must be encouraged.

"We know how to be angry and we know how to be frustrated, but we're afraid to say what it is, why we're angry. Are we angry because we're scared of dying or because we're upset that no one listens to us and we don't know how to say that, or is it a little bit of both?"

Chapter Exercise

This is a difficult exercise to do because it encourages you to expose what you do not like to think about. Do this exercise in the privacy of your room, in the park or at the library, where no one will bother you. We suggest you purchase a notebook, where everything you write will be in one place.

1. Write out a description of the changes in who you are since you have been ill or disabled. If you wish, you may use the diagnosis time period as the turning

point. Try to contrast as sharply and concretely as possible so that you force yourself to think about what has happened to you. Did you like yourself before? How do you feel about yourself now? Why? What changes have occurred in you?

2. Write what it feels like to think of sharing your problems and worries with others. Is it threatening? Why or why not? What do you think others will feel when they hear about your problems? Do you expect different family members to react differently? Friends? People at work?

3. How is your self-esteem? What guidelines do you use to evaluate how you feel about yourself? Do external factors (what others say, how they look at you, etc.) or internal factors (your mood when you awaken, a goal not achieved, etc.) influence you? Have your problems altered your self-esteem in general? Describe how your self-esteem has changed. How has it remained the same?

Try to be as honest in your answers as possible. These exercises are not designed to make great changes in your behavior. They are ways for you to begin exploring difficult material.

Additionally, these exercises will begin to get you familiar with an important tool—journal writing—which will serve you well as you read through this book. Beyond that, many of the people we interviewed emphasized the importance of keeping a journal as a way that allows them to release pent-up emotions. It is a self-contained, self-paced, private way of gaining some control over who you are and where you and your illness are headed. Let these chapter exercises be the start of your journal.

Keeping a Journal

Keeping a journal is an interesting personal experience. So many times in our lives we observe events around us that we would like to remember. We might wish to recall them later to share with others or just to think over ourselves. A journal focusing on stressful periods with chronic illness may seem like a somewhat tedious and repetitive task, but it does not have to be so.

A journal can give us a chance to objectify and make permanent our most personal reactions to life. A person with a chronic illness may have two or three episodes of discomfort in one day. We know it is healthier for that person to express the discomfort during these periods rather than to bury it in memory by repressing it.

A journal entry accomplishes this in a highly effective way. First, the entry provides a retrievable report on an intimate incident. Next, you have an opportunity to report all your reactions without having to deal with anyone else. There also may be other events occurring simultaneously that are interesting and may be related to coping. By itself, the process of thinking, feeling, and writing is therapeutic. You release tension just by putting the words on paper.

Finally, keeping a journal allows you a new way of viewing your own thought processes. You may look back at a journal entry and notice that you process the world in a more complex way than you may have expected. You may have insights and awareness that you did not know you had. You may have sensitivity and openness to experiences that you forgot you had. You may also discover feelings that reactivate your respect for your own human condition. A journal is really an opportunity for a new adventure with yourself, one that can be healing, comforting, and renewing.

Since the primary purpose of the journal involves understanding the "when," "where," and "how" of an illness, it is important to set up some general rules. Here are a few steps to assist you in your journal writing."

1. Get a notebook for this purpose. Make the book small enough so you can carry it with you in your purse or pocket. Start by putting in an entry every day.

2. Try to get in the habit of pulling out the book and writing in it whenever you are uncomfortable.

3. Note the date, time and place when you fill it out. If the situation you are in is too public, step into another room, go outside, or use the bathroom, where privacy is almost guaranteed.

4. Try to include feelings along with a description of the discomfort.

5. If any external or internal events appear to be affecting you, note them.

6. Do not worry about the length or completeness of the entry. As you use your journal, entries will differ dramatically; there is no "correct" length.

It is a good idea to set aside a time at the end of the day that you can use regularly for a summary. If you forgot to write anything or if you had no episodes, be sure to note that at the end of the day or the next morning as soon as you get up. If you have neglected the journal for a few days or longer, don't give up. Just start again. The chronic discomfort or its memory is sure to return!

In a few weeks, the journal will be filled with rich information. It will be useful for medical consults, for self-knowledge and maybe for promoting change. The journal provides you with a new, creative way to monitor your physical problems. It will combat alienation and help to put you in touch with yourself.

When you're up, you're up
And when you're down, you're down.
But when you're only half way up,
You're neither up nor down.
Old Children's Rhyme

Medical problems typically present themselves in overlapping or fluctuating cycles rather than as absent or present. The chronic sufferer is easily swayed, and fear of this suggestibility often interferes with daily activity. It helps to sort out the transient from the serious episodes. Learning to be realistically optimistic is a task that is difficult, but one that must be tackled.

All illnesses evoke anxiety. An illness threatens not only the present but also interferes with the ability to make judgments about the future. As we have seen, the illness or discomfort is a reservoir of unpleasant memories. These recollections—of pain, depression, loneliness, and often despair—contaminate and cloud our view of what is to come.

Because health status changes irregularly, with an uneven pattern, it subjects you to what psychologists call "intermittent negative reinforcement." This is a term used to describe the effect of pain or punishment received erratically and unpredictably.

Psychological research tells us that irregular reinforcement has the most potent effect of any type of punishment. Subjects receiving random doses of discomfort or pain are very high in anxiety at all times. They are unable to predict when pain or discomfort will recur and they remain in a state of constant tension, anticipating the worst.

Likewise, the chronic illness sufferer who is forced to live with unpredictable discomfort is often anxious with anticipation. The anticipation in turn is the basis for an inner sense of helplessness that is always under the surface.

"I had all sorts of plans for my life," says Susan Abeyta, "and then my life went boom [after my mastectomy]. Well, my life could go boom again. I could win the lottery tomorrow, and then I'd do things a little differently. But who knows? Nobody does. So I pay so much more attention—this is so cliche—to the process, rather than the product. But the other shoe can drop any time."

For most people, most medical situations involve a physical condition that has a beginning, a middle, and an end. If you cut your finger, it hurts temporarily, then it heals. When you get a cold, within a few days or a week you usually are well.

But the chronic sufferer does not have this expected and achieved sense of closure. The pattern of the chronic illness is repetitive and overlapping. It is also erratic. Bouts of illness occur in cycles with unpredictable beginnings and ends. The end of a difficult episode may mean that there will be a long break in suffering. Or there may not even be a brief respite before the onset of the next cycle.

"I have little windows of time without pain," says Dorothy McCormick, diagnosed with multiple sclerosis in 1980, "but pain is not on my mind when I'm not feeling pain. I didn't really appreciate that time when I didn't have the pain. People without pain cannot really empathize. You're so delighted when you have that period of time, and you can't get anyone else to empathize if you can't do it yourself. But you always know it'll be back."

As a result, you have three simultaneous battles to contend with:

1. the present suffering

2. the uncertainty of when it will end

3. the uncertainty of when it will begin again (and how intense it will be).

The end of each episode brings on anticipatory anger, loss and grieving even before the new cycle takes hold.

Coping with all three at once, plus the anticipation, can be debilitating. You need emotional strength to actively combat the current cycle, but not become unrealistic or despairing about what lies ahead. An illness that is repetitive and cyclical does not provide the sufferer with the qualitatively steady and predictable life that most people need for planning their daily activities and for maintaining their emotional perspective. So it is not wrong or shameful to feel off-balance. It's the illness doing it to you.

The following is from a journal entry by a nurse with asthma:

"It is 4 A.M. This morning I awaken to greet a new cycle. My lungs prickle and the night is jarred by an early and untimely awakening. I tossed in bed, went to the bathroom, and returned. My body feels alien, restless, ill-at-ease. I lie there wondering what I am doing. I feel like I don't belong in this setting—in this container, my body.

"The side effects of the medication make my skin hurt. My hands feel like I just finished washing hundreds of dishes and the scouring powder ate through to my bones. They look wrinkled and old. I can't see them, but I can visualize them from my touch."

The actual onset of the new cycle does not make it easier to cope with the erratic nature of the pain and the disruptive discomfort. A major problem is the tendency to deny the beginning of the next episode and to fall into despair as it becomes clear that the symptoms are repeating themselves. At the same time, many people feel they have failed themselves and others and are somehow to blame for the new symptoms.

Here's how Sandra McCollum rides out the cycles:

"When home, I begin the process of physical and emotional recovery. I retrain my body to obey simple motor commands (knees, you *will* bend; hands, you *can* grasp). I must also become reoriented to the present. I read newspapers and try to fill in the events of the days I lost in that machine [ventilator].

"To completely put the episode behind me and start living again, I force myself to remember as much as I can of everything that occurred in intensive care. Then I merge my impressions with accounts from other people and form a total picture.

"The circle of recovery is completed when I return to work and fully establish a healthy environment in all aspects of my life. Faith, self-knowledge and determination, support from a physician, home with caring family, work and future hopes—these are the ingredients of my health."

Getting a grasp on the ebb and flow of your discomfort is a useful goal. The more control you gain over the vagaries of your body's turmoil, the less acute your anxiety and frustration will be and the more energy you will have to be proactive rather than reactive. The following exercise is designed with that in mind.

Chapter Exercise

The Discomfort Illometer

Approach this task in a general way. It is actually the first component of several related exercises you will find at the end of subsequent chapters.

To design your own personal illometer, you will need to think of and describe 10 situations in which your physical problems make you uncomfortable. These descriptions should include all the pertinent, familiar ingredients, such as time (morning, afternoon, evening), place (home, office, car, friend's house.), weather (summer, wet, humid, changeable), stress (misplacing a book, missing a TV show, an argument at home, an accident).

Here is a brief example:

"When I work in the yard in the spring my arthritis acts up. I don't think I'm overexerting myself or being too energetic, but I'm not sure. Maybe it's because the ground is damp or because I stay in one position for a long time—

but I always feel deep pain in my back and shoulders afterwards. Maybe it has to do with the time of day?"

Don't feel shy, and don't worry about getting everything down right away. More information will become available later. Remember, it does not have to be a polished product, just a good report of your own special circumstances. These exercises are primarily for you alone, not to share with anyone else in your life.

You may only be able to think of a few episodes, and that is fine. The *process* of doing these exercises will help alter your awareness of events and symptoms. At first it may be difficult to remember the important variables surrounding difficult episode periods, because most people have learned to forget as much as possible about unpleasant experiences. That's how repression works.

This will change as you proceed with the chapters and exercises. In addition, as you look over the 10 episodes, or incidents, you will have some thoughts, insights, and connections that you did not have before. Note them.

After completing the list of 10 situations, or as many as you can think of right now, estimate the degree of discomfort for each item. Rate each item as slight, moderate, or severe discomfort.

Describe as completely as possible the 10 episodes in which you experience discomfort related to your chronic health problem. List as many situations as you can before rating them.

Episode   Rating

1. _____   _____

2. _____   _____

3. _____   _____

4. _____   _____

5. _____   _____

6. _____   _____

7. _____   _____

8. _____   _____

9. _____   _____

10. _____   _____

Now go back and rate the level of discomfort, using the following guide.

Slight (1) — barely perceptible discomfort, a small degree, enough to gain your attention but not enough to focus your thoughts or energy on it.

Moderate (2) — conspicuous discomfort that intrudes and to some degree impinges on the activities you pursue or plan to pursue.

Severe (3) — extremely disruptive discomfort that significantly changes your activity pattern, including altering your activity plans.

Now, stop and think what new insights you have gained by completing this exercise. Later chapters will include other methods of record keeping—Weekly Chart (Chapter 4) and Personal Awareness Interference Number (Chapter 5)—which will build on what you've learned here.

> One's own self is well hidden
> from one's own self.
>
> **Nietzsche**

Keeping track of your illness is a demanding, continuous—indeed, chronic—task. But it must be done. This chapter shows you how and why.

Let us imagine a patient with a chronic illness going to the doctor for a regular check-up.

The doctor peers intently at the patient and asks, "How are you doing?"

The patient shifts uneasily, looks at the floor, and mumbles, "Fine, just fine."

The doctor runs through a series of specific questions about symptoms related to the illness. The patient denies any problems. The doctor continues through a routine examination. Finished, she pats the patient on the back.

"I'll see you in a month for your next check-up. Keep up the good work."

It's a familiar, almost comforting, routine. Perhaps it is too routine—for both the doctor and the patient. The patient leaves and returns to the waiting room, where his wife, anticipating completion of the examination, greets him.

"Well, how did it go?"

"Okay."

"Did you tell her how bad you felt last week?"

"No."

"You didn't tell her you had trouble sleeping those nights you kept me up? She doesn't know how bad your stomach was Sunday?"

"No."

At this point, his wife is frustrated—and annoyed.

"Well, I don't get it." Her irritation is barely contained. "All week you complained about the pain and how nervous you are about what might be wrong, and then when you finally see your doctor, you don't say a damned thing?"

The patient is despondent. "I always forget when I get in there. I just can't keep my head clear with the doctor in the room. When she comes in, I feel anxious. She always seems in a rush. I get confused." He sighs resignedly. "I just think about getting out."

"Maybe next time you should write down the things that go wrong," she says a bit more sympathetically. "You know, keep track of stuff before you see the doctor again. There must be some way to let her know what's going on."

This brief scene is not unusual. People with health problems find themselves confused and inaccurate at times in the doctor's office. For those with a chronic illness, it is even harder to keep track of the long, complex patterns of their difficulties.

The numerous ups and downs and the idiosyncracies can be overwhelming. The erratic, unpredictable sequences add to the monitoring problems. A great deal of persistence and discipline is necessary to track symptoms over time. Such a task forces you to confront the facts of the disability—often a demoralizing and frustrating undertaking.

Why is this so hard? The difficulty appears to have two causes. The first is the patience required. The second is the unconscious hiding, or masking, of what has occurred, something health professionals call *repression*.

Let's start with patience. Psychological research has shown that persons with chronic illness vary greatly. For some, fatigue and stress affect the degree of discomfort. For others, time of day, varying food intake, or kinds of activities affect the illness. For still others, the weather or other environmental variables can change the course of an illness. It is important to understand there is no shortcut to figuring out how all this operates for any one person.

Sometimes, keeping a chart, a journal, or a workbook of important events can help your doctor better understand the vagaries of your personal relationship to your disease. Jotting down your feelings and anxieties can also be a good emotional release. It is a way of calming your worry that you might forget to tell the doctor something you think is important.

The benefits of writing down your feelings often are not apparent until you have done it for a while. Some people feel they will seem foolish writing down material about their illness. They believe that the best thing to do with such problems is to ignore them.

But if you chart the ups and downs regularly, positive results can occur. Also, by putting them on paper, you can go back and reread what you have written, making it easier to see the variations and place your feelings in perspective. The overview can be enlightening and invigorating. Here is an example given to us by a 67-year-old patient:

"Every time the phone would ring after supper, I'd jump. It was usually my 31- year-old son pestering me: Did I take my medicine yet? Did I call the doctor today? Can I move my hands better?

"I know he wanted to help, but before I even picked up the receiver, my head ached and my fingers got stiffer. And, how could I tell him the medicine made me sick, so I didn't take any today? That usually gets him angry.

"I was so upset, I'd pace back and forth while we talked on the phone. That made me tired, and I became more irritable. Sometimes, I just hung up on him. I resented him calling. I felt terrible."

What to do? The fact was that he sometimes didn't take his prescribed medicine. His son's concerns were genuine and they did have some foundation. We suggested that he keep track of his symptoms and medications in a daily chart. He then shared the chart entries with his son, who was relieved and pleased. As a result, the father-son phone calls became less confrontational.

Because keeping a chart requires a concerted effort, you are forced to pay attention to how you feel at home, while traveling, at work and at leisure. A pencil and pad are the only tools required. (If writing is a physical problem for you, you can use a manual or voice-activated tape recorder.) Already burdened with physical problems, you may see this as just another energy-consuming exercise. Indeed, it is easy at first not to recognize the benefits. We will help you identify them.

Lack of patience is not the only obstacle to recording change. The second potent force is the defense mechanism called *repression*. Repression is a mental activity that psychologists and psychiatrists say involves the unconscious burying or pushing away of unpleasant experiences or feelings.

Similar to denial, repression enables us to avoid anxiety-provoking thoughts. It allows us to concentrate on other matters that are less stressful and provide us with more pleasure. This defense is useful in many situations because without it we might find ourselves constantly thinking about disturbing events. The constant focusing might make it hard to do our work, to be involved with others, or to find healthy ways to get on with our lives.

While repression can be useful, it also can cost a great deal emotionally. When we block out upsetting events and their accompanying feelings, we may also filter out important information. In the case of a chronic illness, the monitoring of the ebb and flow of the illness can be very illuminating. In a way, it enables you to become a researcher and recorder in the area of your own disability.

In fact, you are really the ultimate expert on the impact of the problem. Only you can follow the subjective course of the illness—the feeling or experiencing part of what is affecting your life. A doctor or nurse can measure external signs and symptoms. But you can learn to report many of these, too.

The importance of learning to be conversant with your symptomatology and subjective experiences goes beyond being able to communicate accurately and confidently to your doctor. It is also of real consequence because it helps you take aim at your ability and desire to gain control and direction over how you are treated, medically and otherwise. In fact, it has a direct bearing on how you and your partner, the illness, will fare.

The people we interviewed have strong views on the matter. Mary Alice Kerr, for instance.

"You really [need to] try to know what's going on. Know your condition. Know your symptoms. Be assertive," she advises. Accumulating this knowledge and making note of it has secondary, but important, purposes as well, she points out. "You may encounter health providers in emergency situations who are unfamiliar with your history and the procedures you require. You might need to give them instructions on how to help you."

In choosing the right medical caregiver, it is instructive to assess the role of the doctor. As Mary Alice, diagnosed with multiple sclerosis in early 1991, implies, not all doctors meet her criteria. The physician she trusts is "compassionate, responsive, patient, she listens [and] thinks enough about things. She cares about whether or not she feels she is helping me."

Sandra McCollum has had similar good fortune. She was particularly taken by the fact that her doctor "included *me* in the therapy. He cared about my priorities and goals in life. He learned how important my family and job are to me, that I read everything from Shakespeare to Jonathan Winters, root for the Lakers and Dodgers, and grow roses."

And he also learned that Sandra was not afraid to die. She made it clear she would refuse to be kept alive on a respirator if it meant "being sustained on a machine past the point when I can return to life and laughter."

That point almost came one day in 1987. Her doctor stepped to the side of her hospital bed to listen to her lungs, dangerously weakened and worn out from decades of battle.

"This time I was ready," she remembers. "Too much of my life was being spent in dreading these terrible episodes, and I felt it would be better for everyone if I didn't survive." Her doctor moved to the front of the bed and faced her.

"He looked at me and told me honestly that soon I would be unconscious and would die if he did not intubate me. Then he reinforced his earlier agreement that he would not go against my wishes if I still refused. He said simply, *'Please let me help you.'*"

With these words he had put Sandra before any clinical considerations and he had given back all the free will that a machine and unfeeling physicians had usurped for years. "Because somehow he had understood that I was ready to make the only choice I felt I had left in this life, he returned to me the entire range of choosing, and so treated my body and healed my agony at the same time.

"A doctor," Sandra reflects with quiet passion, "who adds human being to his medical credentials has helped me to live in health."

Clearly, monitoring your health is a personal issue and one that includes a motivated doctor. Since most of us would welcome a doctor with those qualities, why are they so hard to find?

The mission of the doctor is to heal the sick and to relieve physical suffering. Thoroughly trained within that context, frustration is likely to result whenever a situation arises that provides little or no opportunity to decrease the patient's discomfort, cure the illness, or control the medical problem.

Enter the person with a chronic illness. The illness does not disappear with a proper treatment. Although its effects can sometimes be contained or lessened, there is a high probability that the struggles will continue throughout life. Furthermore, there is a high probability that the patient will require intermittent assistance from the doctor, who is not immune to the ultimate fear of death from the illness.

The doctor has an unpleasant task. In some way, the doctor has to promote in the patient a willingness to follow medical instructions and attend to symptoms even though there is no "cure" for the problem. Many doctors, not to mention patients, find this frustrating and unrewarding.

It can be a combustible situation. The patient is angry (at the doctor, at himself, at the cosmos) because the illness is not, and cannot be, cured. The doctor is frustrated and angered at his "incompetence" for being unable to conclusively help his patient, to use the knowledge his training ostensibly prepared him for. The result: a high likelihood of ambivalence about the doctor/patient relationship.

Some doctors, like Mary Alice Kerr's and Sandra McCollum's, have a blend of knowledge and compassion that enables them to inspire and direct chronic patients effectively. Such a doctor has to have accepted the fallibility of the medical field, the complexity of life with an incurable illness, and the need to provide the patient with perspective and hope.

These are difficult tasks, and many doctors are not able to contend with them. As a result, frustrated and angered by the intractable illness that will not go away or stay under control, some doctors avoid contact with the chronic patient and sometimes are curt in their interactions with them.

So you must be alert to the obstacles that may already be erected at the door to the doctor's office. In every instance that you hold back a full report of symptomatology, or the doctor hurries or ignores you, there is a real possibility that the illness will progress and important communication will deteriorate.

"I have found in dealing with people in hospitals, and then looking at my own health, nobody cares as much about my health as I do," says Rebecca Steinberg. "I have to take the responsibility for what's going on with my own body. You have to be assertive.... I always tell people: 'Don't be passive. Let everybody know you're there. Don't let them mistreat you.'"

Or, as Susan Abeyta puts it, "I really do want to know—I don't want bullshit."

So, yes, it is easy to become confused in the doctor's office when it is time to report on weeks or months of physical functioning. It is frustrating trying to describe in detail a complex series of improvements and setbacks over a period of time. "Well, it got better, then it got worse and a little better for a short while until yesterday just before lunch, I think . . . ."

When you keep a record of the changes in an illness, it is easier to see the course of the symptoms over time and across many events. A chart is a good way to do this. It must be tailored to your illness and experience, and you will have to begin to become sensitive to all the factors that can affect your medical status.

Keeping the chart will not be easy to do. If you can work on a few preparatory exercises, you will have increased sensitivity to the aspects of the illness that can be readily charted and recorded.

In summary, the idea is to (1) learn how to recognize and communicate the changes going on in your body; (2) report them; and (3) build your confidence so that you report everything of significance to the doctor on your next office visit, with or without your spouse accompanying you.

Chapter Exercise

Weekly Chart

In the beginning, the Weekly Chart will require time and practice. While it may appear overwhelming at first, most chart users quickly become accustomed to the daily routine. Remember, too, that your work with the Discomfort Illometer in the previous chapter has already given you solid experience with self-reporting methods.

With some practice, you can also capture the events occurring around the onset of your discomfort as well as the post-symptomatic experience itself. Taken together, the overall goal is to be able to tell what helps immediately, what helps over time, and what does not help at all.

We have divided the page into four parts: night, morning, afternoon, and evening. Each part is to be filled in with three entries: description of symptoms and a rating of symptoms on two dimensions—*symptom intensity* and *symptom intrusion.*

Symptom intensity is the range and severity of the discomfort.

0 — not present

1 — low or intermittent intensity

2 — moderate or constant intensity

3 — high level and extreme intensity

Symptom intrusion is the degree to which the symptom interferes with your normal activities.

0 — does not interfere

1 — slight or intermittent interference

2 — moderate and constant low-level interference

3 — extreme and immobilizing interference

The entire week will be evaluated day by day, and each day will be divided into parts. (See examples on pages 45 and 46.)

For now, notes are needed but they should be abbreviated so the Weekly Chart does not become unwieldly. To help you, we have included a list of factors as a guide. The list is broken down into eight categories, or variables. Each symptom should include at least one item from each category. It may interest you to know that doctors, psychologists and most other health care professionals incorporate these factors, and more, into their assessment processes before making a diagnosis.

After two weeks of daily charting, stop and review your notes. Look for patterns that relate to symptoms— for example, time of day, alone or with others, particular activities, foods, etc. To help you remember, use the old journalism device, Who, What, When, Where, Why, How.

Keep in mind that this is a *guide*. Feel free to add your own factors.

Factors to Be Noted in Charts on Pages 47-51

(P) Place
Home
Work
On transportation
Kitchen
Bedroom
At a movie
Restroom
Don't know/don't
  remember
Other

(F) Feeling
Fatigue
Anxiety
Depression
Excitement
Pressure
Joy
Anticipation
Relief
Guilt
Anger
Other

(T) Time

Morning
Noon
Afternoon
Evening
Night
Before dawn

(S) Social

With child(ren)
With male
With female
With friend
With boss
With co-worker
With parent(s)
With salesperson
Alone
Other

(A) Activity

Rising
Dressing
Preparing food
Eating
Speaking on phone
Preparing to travel
Driving car
Shopping
Gardening
Working
Other

(B) Body Functions

Pre-meal
During meal
Post-meal
Pre-sex
During sex
Post-sex
Pre-toilet
Not relevant
None
Other

(E) Emotion	(SL) Stress Level
Laughing	None
Drinking	Low
Fighting	Moderate
Intense reaction	High
Minor/major accident	Transition
Surprise	Uncertain
Tension	
Crying	
Remembering stress	
Overjoy	
Other	

The Weekly Chart gives you enough room to fill in physically distressing events throughout each day. Use the chart with time slots (pp. 45-50) or one in which no time frame is indicated (p. 51), whichever is most comfortable for you. You can enter one or several episodes for each part of the day. It is important that each entry be rated by symptom intensity and symptom intrusion.

(At the end of each day, the information you have noted on the Weekly Chart will be used to arrive at a Personal Awareness Interference Number [PAIN], which will enable you to compare the ups and downs of every 24-hour period. Calculating the PAIN level is the exercise in the next chapter.)

Remember: The comments filled in on the Weekly Chart should note the activities going on *during* the symptom appearance (and immediately before or after), including what seems to improve the symptom state.

44

How to Use the Weekly Chart

(Example 1 - Experiencing Back Pain at Home)

Period of the Day	Description of Symptoms	Symptom Intensity (0-3)	Symptom Intrusion (0-3)
10 a.m. - noon (Factors - from pages 42 - 44) Place: at home Time: morning Social: alone Feeling: depressed Activity: TV Body: pre-meal Emotion: none Stress: low	It's my lower back again – always in the morning (but not every day) – only when I'm thinking about what I'm going to do today – watching TV helps, but not enough.	(2) moderate	(2) moderate

(Example 2 - Breathing Problems While Out Socializing)

Period of the Day	Description of Symptoms	Symptom Intensity (0-3)	Symptom Intrusion (0-3)
6 p.m. - 8 p.m. (Factors - from pages 42 - 44) Place: in car Time: night Social: w/friends Feeling: anticipation Activity: driving Body: none Emotion: remembering stress Stress: moderate	Breathing difficulties once again –is it the muggy night air or excitement being with my friends? It scares me, whatever it is – reminds me of time I had to go to the hospital.	(1) low	(0) low

How to Use the Weekly Chart

(Example 3 - Experiencing Arthritic Pain at Work)

Period of the Day	Description of Symptoms	Symptom Intensity (0-3)	Symptom Intrusion (0-3)
2 p.m. - 4 p.m. (Factors - from pages 42 - 44) Place: at work Time: afternoon Social: with colleagues Feeling: anxious Activity: working at computer Body: fatigue Emotion: tension Stress: transition	It's that damn shoulder pain again – will I have to leave work early? And what about that tennis tournament this weekend? Will I have to cancel that too? What a pain – in more ways than one!	(2) moderate	(3) high

Weekly Chart

Day No. _____

Note: Make copies of this page as needed before beginning.

Date _____ Day of Week _____ Weather _____

Period of the Day	Description of Symptoms	Symptom Intensity (0-3)	Symptom Intrusion (0-3)
Night **Midnight - 6 a.m.**			
(Factors - from pages 42 - 44) **12 - 2 a.m.** Place: Time: Social: Feeling: Activity: Body: Emotion: Stress: **2 a.m. - 4 a.m.** Place: Time: Social: Feeling: Activity: Body: Emotion: Stress: **4 a.m. - 6 a.m.** Place: Time: Social: Feeling: Activity: Body: Emotion: Stress:			

Weekly Chart
Day No. _____

Note: Make copies of this page as needed before beginning.

Date _____ Day of Week _____ Weather _____

Period of the Day	Description of Symptoms	Symptom Intensity (0-3)	Symptom Intrusion (0-3)
Morning **6 a.m. - Noon**			
(Factors - from pages 42 - 44) **6 a.m. - 8 a.m.** Place: Time: Social: Feeling: Activity: Body: Emotion: Stress: **8 a.m. - 10 a.m.** Place: Time: Social: Feeling: Activity: Body: Emotion: Stress: **10 a.m. - noon** Place: Time: Social: Feeling: Activity: Body: Emotion: Stress:			

Weekly Chart

Day No. _____

Note: Make copies of this page as needed before beginning.

Date _____ Day of Week _____ Weather _____

Period of the Day	Description of Symptoms	Symptom Intensity (0-3)	Symptom Intrusion (0-3)
Afternoon **Noon - 6 p.m.**			
(Factors - from pages 42 - 44) **noon - 2 p.m.** Place: Time: Social: Feeling: Activity: Body: Emotion: Stress: **2 p.m. - 4 p.m.** Place: Time: Social: Feeling: Activity: Body: Emotion: Stress: **4 p.m. - 6 p.m.** Place: Time: Social: Feeling: Activity: Body: Emotion: Stress:			

Weekly Chart

Day No. _____

Note: Make copies of this page as needed before beginning.

Date _____ Day of Week _____ Weather _____

Period of the Day	Description of Symptoms	Symptom Intensity (0-3)	Symptom Intrusion (0-3)
Evening 6 p.m. - Midnight			
(Factors - from pages 42 - 44)			
6 p.m. - 8 p.m. Place: Time: Social: Feeling: Activity: Body: Emotion: Stress:			
8 p.m. - 10 p.m. Place: Time: Social: Feeling: Activity: Body: Emotion: Stress:			
10 p.m. - Midnight Place: Time: Social: Feeling: Activity: Body: Emotion: Stress:			

Weekly Chart
(Open-ended Time)

Note: Make copies of this page as needed before beginning.

Date _____ Day of Week _____ Weather _____

(Factors - from pages 42 - 44)	Description of Symptoms	Symptom Intensity (0-3)	Symptom Intrusion (0-3)

5. Preparing for Battle

A wise man should consider that health
is the greatest of human blessing, and
learn how by his own thoughts to derive
benefit from his illness.

Hippocrates

Chronic illness presents new behavioral challenges, both unwanted and unexpected. Change can be exhausting and preparation may seem impossible. Daily life looms as insurmountable. Others are not aware of the internal dialogue taking place. A practical worksheet will be provided to help you identify, and respond to, the activities that elicit the mental struggles.

"Sometimes I forget I have diabetes," says Emma Hart. "I'll take my blood level and it will be up. I say, 'Wow. You'd think I have diabetes or something.'"

Emma, a diabetes educator, was diagnosed with Type 2 diabetes in November 1980. Like others we interviewed for this book, it took some time for her to adjust to her new medical condition. Now, she's firmly in control. Changes in her diabetes, which she manages with diet and exercise, help give substance and direction to her day.

"I use it—my diabetes—as a tool," she says. "It's as important as the computer or the telephone."

For 52-year-old Anna Wu, who has had Type 1 diabetes for 35 years, the tool is structure and planning.

Anna, whose left leg was amputated in 1984, arranges her daily routine to include what she calls an "activity of the day." She says, "It's so important to get up, get dressed and have something to do."

She acknowledges, "There are times—two, three days in a row sometimes—when I feel sorry for myself. I won't deny that. But you do the most with what you've got.

"I'd rather do more than less. You usually can find a new avenue when one is closed, a new way of doing things. Something always comes from branching out."

Here is a sample of Anna Wu's activities of the day, with her own explanation of their importance to her.

Monday—duplicate bridge. ("Because I have to be off my feet.")

Tuesday—bridge lessons, lunch with friends. ("I consciously keep in touch with friends. I need them more than they need me.")

Wednesday—continuing education classes, lunch. ("I escape in books. I lose myself in what I'm reading. I don't necessarily like to read books about problems similar to mine.")

Thursday—board meeting or volunteer work at the hospital, lunch. ("I never come away from the hospital not feeling better.")

Friday—hairdresser, lunch; evening out with gentleman friend. ("I have a real normal life, even with all these things wrong with me.")

To break the routine on occasion, Anna goes shopping.

"I like to get out of my situation," she explains. "I walk around the store and change the scene. I also go to the pancake house or the pharmacy. I remove myself from the surrounding scenery. It helps to get some wind blowing through your hair."

Our experience and research suggest that any situation that requires or causes you to anticipate change, adaptation, or readjustment can be potentially stressful. This includes both positive and negative experiences: moving to a new home, expecting a grandchild, getting a divorce, planning a trip. Family crises, special events, vacations, personal and financial losses all contain hidden threats, a sure sign of potential stress.

Fortunately, you already have a well-earned ration of adaptive methods for dealing with these internal pressures. Some of us postpone acting until we have regained our composure or perspective. Others retreat, providing an opportunity to allow the elements of the change to be digested and examined. Still others charge headlong into the challenge and resolve it quickly.

In each case, the goal must be to reduce the likelihood or possibility that things will take you by surprise. Don't just follow the pain, allowing it to assert its control and set the agenda. Reach for something that will in effect make the pain work for you in some way.

"Pain makes me less frivolous then I used to be," says artist Ken Saville, 43. "It sharpened my focus. I tend to want to do things that are important to me." In particular, Ken, who was diagnosed with polio at birth, likes spending his time with children, teaching them to enjoy creating works of art.

"It's a concentrated thing. When I'm so wrapped up in it, nothing can overcome the joy I get from the kids. When outside forces are intruding, I give them attention, and my pain goes away almost immediately."

"Fatigue is as steady and close as my shadow," says Karen Stone, 45, "so I make sure it doesn't get too long by working on my Ph.D. in catnapping. I maneuver the frustrations, like sitting on the ground while digging a hole, instead of falling. I avoid emotional stress by nipping things in the bud instead of allowing buildups. And I let myself laugh deeper these days."

It is important that you come to terms with the one thing that is unchanging: The battle is always present. It will always be there—the push and pull of striving forward versus the nagging background hum, sometimes audible, sometimes excluded from immediate awareness, tempting you to give up.

"There's something in who I am that doesn't let me give in," Susan Abeyta asserts. "Some people are stronger than other people. When I felt despair, I felt despair. When I was feeling sick, I was sick. But when I wasn't, I was up and about. I read. I had really good friends without whom I would never have survived."

"You really want to make sure that people know what you can do, instead of just what you can't do," Peter Clifton, a 35-year-old paraplegic, believes. "It works out better that way for everyone. Once you get into that mindset, it takes some of the limits off you."

Thinking about it, you can see that all of us have a particular style which we apply to life's stresses. One task right now is to determine how you usually cope with change and the resultant stress.

1. Are you the kind of person who likes things to be orderly, regular, and controlled? Or do you like

things to be spontaneous and flexible, with many alternatives?

2. Are you the kind of person who likes to take life one day at a time? Or do you like to know in advance what will happen in the immediate and the distant future?

3. Are you the kind of person who likes to concentrate all your energies on one project? Or do you like to do several things at once?

4. Are you the kind of person who likes consistency and predictability in life? Or do you prefer variability and uncertainty?

It is important to remember that change can be both invigorating and debilitating—sometimes at the same time. To minimize the resulting stress, it is often a good idea to (1) work out a plan of action beforehand; (2) proceed in outlined, easy-to-complete steps; and (3) keep a backup plan in reserve for emergencies.

Neil Bischkoff's allergies forced him to prepare in just that manner. An active child, he was compelled to take note of his condition in his college years. He discovered that tree pollen and final exams for the spring semester tended to coincide.

"I spent the last two or three years of finals in bed," he remembers. "I knew I couldn't study during finals, so I arranged my studying for before then. I just didn't plan on studying during final exams. I had to prepare for everything all year." His allergies later evolved into asthma. Neil eventually became a doctor.

Karen Stone prepares by "working smarter," as she puts it. "In the office, for example, instead of making several individual trips, I gather my paperwork via my destination and accomplish several tasks in one trip. In doing all of the above, I try to sustain a balance, being as active as possible without creating too much fatigue."

In many mountainous areas, there are safety outlets for runaway vehicles. Recognizing that brakes fail and that drivers misjudge speed limits or become fatigued, highway departments provide sites at the side of the road to allow both drivers and vehicles to "rest." These roadside stops can serve as a good metaphor for chronic illness sufferers who find themselves having difficulty coping with change, both expected and unexpected. When you feel the pace or flow of change is getting out of control, it is a wise idea to have in reserve an "off-ramp" that allows you to catch your breath, check your gauges, and regain your steadiness. Then, and only then, should you return to the highways.

Chapter Exercise
Personal Awareness Interference Number (PAIN)

For this exercise, you will need to make use of the Symptom Intensity and Symptom Intrusion information your learned about in the previous chapter. You are now ready to take your self-monitoring one step further. At the end of each day, for each incident of discomfort, multiply the Symptom Intensity rating by the Symptom Intrusion

rating to get an Individual Perception Unit (INPUT).
Total INPUTs will be your daily Personal Awareness
Interference Number, or PAIN.

	Intensity	Intrusion
Ache in shoulder	(2)	(3)

2 x 3 = 6 (Individual Perception Unit—INPUT)

Now add all the INPUTs for each day to get your daily
Personal Awareness Interference Number (PAIN).

Example

Sunday						
		Intensity		**Intrusion**		**INPUT**
8:00 .A.M.	Ache in shoulder	2	x	3	=	6
10:30 A.M.	Stiffness in elbow	1	x	2	=	2
12:05 P.M.	Joint ache	2	x	3	=	6
2:50 P.M.	Joint ache	1	x	1	=	1
7:20 P.M.	Ache in shoulder	2	x	3	=	6

PAIN Score = 21 for Sunday

As you will see, it is useful to compare changes in your
discomfort level over time. It is a concrete way of helping
you understand how your illness or disability is affecting
you over a measurable period. The Pain Graph on page 60
has been devised to assist you. To use the graph, you must
choose 5 INPUT scores per day. Add the scores (Daily
PAIN Scores) and use the total for each day's entry on the

graph. After doing this for several weeks, you will begin to note interesting patterns and variations, such as changes in number of episodes per week, alterations in the intensity of the episodes at certain times, and differences in your responses.

You will also gain a more global understanding of how your disability or illness affects your daily life and the lives of those around you. In all, you should gain the ability to judge when and in what circumstances discomfort is likely to occur, thus enabling you to prepare alternative or backup choices for the day's activities.

You may be surprised by the results.

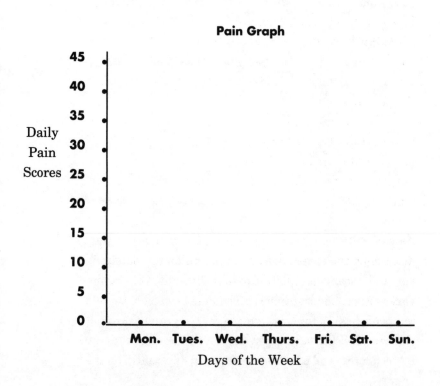

The strongest of all warriors are
these two—Time and Patience
Tolstoy

*Sick people in our society are seen as faulty. To add to the
burden, the mass media promote the non-necessity of
suffering. Moreover, sickness elicits denial in our culture.
As a result, chronic sufferers are doubly damned—feeling
guilty from within and feeling misunderstood and criticized from outside. Fighting back, and how to handle the
emotions from this "culture conflict," will be focused upon
in this chapter.*

In *Through The Looking-Glass*, Lewis Carroll captures
the dilemma we discuss in this chapter. He describes the
encounter between the Red Queen and Alice. With no
warning, the Queen suddenly grabs Alice's hand, and
they begin to run.

The Queen tells Alice repeatedly to go "Faster!
Faster!" But "Alice felt she could not go faster, though she
had but no breath left to say so." Finally, "they went so fast
that at last they seemed to skim through the air, hardly
touching the ground with their feet, till suddenly...they
stopped."

Alice realizes that they are in the same place as they
were when they started. She complains that in her country "... you'd generally get to somewhere else if you ran
very fast ...." The Queen replies sneeringly, "A slow sort
of country ...! Now, here, you see, it takes all the running
you can do, to keep in the same place. If you want to get

somewhere else, you must run at least twice as fast as that!"

Carroll's wisdom reflects on two messages to anyone who does not fit in. The messages are especially toxic to someone with a physical problem. First, you are not quite up to par, and there must be something wrong with you if you are different. Second, the only solution to not fitting in is to adjust, adapt, and rush to keep up. Let's explore these two messages and see how they affect you.

We live in a culture that glorifies speed, action, beauty, health, and youth. The news, commercials, popular literature, and movies all reflect the exaltation of the strong and the sleek. Although some changes have occurred in recent years, particularly through the political forcefulness of the disabled themselves, there still is a general prejudice against weakness or illness of any kind. Appearances are important.

"I learned real fast that you're punished if you have a chronic disease," Sandra McCollum recalls. "I was turned down for jobs. I had to lie on my application to college because they wouldn't have let me live in the dorm if they had known.

"It's really only in the last three years that I've kind of come out of the closet with any of this. . . . I guess it's because I've felt safe and I'm working with a group of people who accept me, not because I'm sick or not sick.

"I don't view myself as a sick person. I think of myself as a healthy person who on occasion gets sick."

There are several unspoken messages tied to the dismissal of illness and these are mirrored in the Queen's disdainful, "A slow sort of country. . . !" One message is that sick people deserve to be sick because they are not living their lives in a healthy fashion. This communication, usually offered by a well person, implies that if you follow the rules for bodily care and respect, you will not become ill. If you are ill, the reasoning goes, you have abused your body and deserve the illness. This viewpoint places you on the defensive.

Susan Abeyta remembers the emotions she felt after her mastectomy in early 1989. She had heard and read that those in her situation were somehow to blame for their illness. Carrying that burden, she says, was like "climbing up a steep mountain. Someone says you can save your life; all you have to do is change it. You can be an exceptional patient."

Susan says she carried around a tape in her head that said, "'I'm not good enough.' Now I was going to die because I wasn't good enough. That was tough—dying of having a bad attitude. It was nothing to do with 'good enough.' Here is the answer—the truth is, there is no answer. There is no one way. There is only what works for you.

"We have a thousand ways to blame the victim. People need to feel they have control over what happens to them. Blaming them doesn't give them control."

Karyn Muir, 38, has diabetes. She is succinct. Asked if she has encountered the message that she is responsible for her illness, Karyn protests. "They're crazy if they think it's my fault."

Others maintain that illness reflects a person's inability to handle the environment and the consequent emotional reactions. This view is part of the philosophy that well-adjusted people do not get anxious, angry or frustrated and therefore they do not get sick. If you are sick, this perspective suggests, you have an emotional problem. Again, this view puts you on the defensive.

Another viewpoint, a hybrid of religion and morality, asserts that illness is a punishment for sins committed. This belief has historical roots in certain early religions. The sick person, suffering for a crime against God, self, or others in the community, is treated with disdain and pity.

Some people cannot tolerate being around those who are sick, although they do not adopt any of the three perspectives just noted. Some of these people carry with them childhood superstitions. During those early years, witnessing a bad event or being in a frightening place evoked fears of contagion, i.e., if you touch a toad, you catch warts; if you get too close to someone who has any kind of malady, you will acquire the same illness.

This kind of logic is complemented by the primitive notion that if we do not think about an upsetting idea, it cannot affect us. Remember the three monkeys: See no evil, hear no evil, speak no evil. Something like a negative vaccination, this view supposes that if we are unaware of another's illness, we cannot be affected by it.

Finally, a natural human reaction to another person's weakness and complaints is to think of our own vulnerability. We all find ourselves, in various ways, facing our mortality and the impermanence of our bodies. The healthy person may see yours as sick and getting old, and may anxiously move away from you to get distance and "safety."

To be told that we must accept the highly offensive idea that we may be the recipient of randomly distributed good and bad happenings, disturbs our sense of justice. Illness and injury affect all families. One certainty we have is that the longer we live, the more suffering and pain we will have to confront. But we also can search for joyful experiences.

People who are ill sometimes elicit other people's fears, defenses, and unfounded notions about illness. Ironically, as people run away from you, they are trying to run away from the truth—truth about their vulnerability and truth about coping with illness and disability. As a result, they are ill prepared for the inevitable physical problems that will arise with their own bodies. You, however, will be ready for whatever may come next.

The Queen, you will recall, told Alice, "It takes all the running you can do to keep in the same place. . . ." Television commercials, movies, newspapers, and magazines tell us that days that hold the maximum amount of activity are the best ("Grab all the gusto you can!"). This message is a potential trap for those trying to keep things in perspective and live in a healthy manner. The person with a chronic illness or disability cannot afford to join the fast-action parade. It is easy, and understandably tempting, to want to take leave of your pain and discomfort immediately. To maintain your well-being, however, you must determine the pace of life from within, not from without.

Peter Clifton, injured in a motorcycle accident, reports a pertinent conversation with a man in a wheelchair:

"He told me that he had to get past this thing in the back of his mind that says, 'I'm going to wake up tomorrow and be okay.' Until you get rid of that, you're not going to go anywhere. You feel like you just can't wait. You drive yourself absolutely batty. I couldn't wait...it was becoming a real stumbling block.

"You don't ever really get rid of it, but you have to learn to take it day by day. You have to figure out what this means. It doesn't mean you can't plan ahead. Six months from now, I'm going to go to Costa Rica, hopefully. But in the meantime, you've still got to do each day as it comes. It would ruin the trip to Costa Rica if I said I'll be walking in six months. That's *verboten* territory, I guess."

The person struggling to maintain physical wellness, as well as mental wellness, has to fight off the influence of social hysteria to stay busy continually, to be publicly and visibly in control. The true ideal is a personal rhythm that is sensitively and carefully choreographed to work for you.

Let us consider one option. Because of the cyclical nature of your illness, some days and times are more motivating than others. Thus, it makes sense, as always, to attend to what your body is telling you. One way to do this, and in fact to take advantage of your body's self-paced advice, is to develop alternative ways of moving through your day, depending on your level of wellness. You might consider, for example, having slow-paced days and relatively fast-paced days.

On slow-paced days, you can be ready to complete the day with a lower level of expectation. If you find yourself feeling bad at any point during the day, consider that a message that it's time to minimize work, slow down your activities, and decrease your expectations of yourself. You might want to look for those activities that do not require as much movement, action, and change.

In addition, you should think about simplifying any travel plans (even those just across town), meal arrangements, social engagements, and transitions between activities. You might want to have a good book or TV program lined up so you can rest and relax. If possible, you should try to be sure in advance that your work schedule has as many alternatives as possible. That way, you can more easily downshift to accommodate those physically difficult days when they occur.

It is also probably a good idea to leave rest space between work periods. You can choose to tell people around you that this is a slower-paced day. Co-workers with chronic illnesses themselves will understand. Others, as we have seen, may very well be less responsive.

If you can accept this approach, you might begin to accomplish many things in an even, unhurried fashion. Writing letters and reports, filing, sorting, organizing, planning, completing old work, reviewing previous efforts, making telephone calls, and paying bills are all ideal for these times. This method can work only if you are in a flexible environment and you prepare ahead of time. Then, when a slow day emerges, you will greet it with less irritation and sadness because your alternative agenda will be ready and in place.

On faster-paced days, when you are feeling energetic, you can move mountains. Your actions still should have some order, but you have more energy available to meet your daily demands. Household chores, play, driving, errands, meeting people, confronting difficult situations, and engaging in lively leisure pursuits can become parts of your day.

These two formats are extremes. Of course, there are middle-of-the-road paces as well. The true value in the concept of the varied pace lies in changing your daily expectations in a realistic way. You are neither an automaton nor a superperson. You will get more done and experience less frustration if you accurately assess what's possible or not possible.

If your options are limited by your work situation or because of an intense, difficult home environment, try to use this system for your leisure time. You can get up early and make breakfast in slow motion when your body is working less efficiently. You can drive to work early at a comfortable pace, if you choose to do so.

You can prepare meals (make two or three in advance and put them in the freezer so you'll have them on the days when your energy is low), get preventive auto maintenance done, have cash on hand, babysitters available, a comfortable place to put your legs up after standing. All of these can be in place and ready to use in rough times.

Also in the realm of slow-paced versus fast-paced living is prior notice to friends that you may not always be able to follow through on plans made in advance. It is important to be able to alter plans with friends and not feel guilty—or worse, to feel pushed into doing something you don't feel up to doing right now.

Your pace must reflect your decisions, or you, like

Alice, will feel as if you are racing to stay in the same place.

We offer two other suggestions for you to consider in this broad picture of pace. The first is the use of realistic goals based on small steps.

Completing goals in small steps sounds simple enough, but it is not so easy to do. If you have a big job to complete, breaking it down into small, manageable portions is a wise decision. That way, you stay in charge and can track your progress in segments.

If your goal is to clean your garage, plant a garden, study computers, earn a degree, learn a piece of music, travel cross-country, or buy Christmas presents, using a step-at-a-time procedure encourages you to proceed at your own pace. You can feel the accomplishment of one milestone adding on to another. You begin to see yourself as someone who moves with a quiet and steady flow. The end product can be venturesome or basic.

"I didn't know if I was going to get better," recalls Kathryn Stuart, 67, after being diagnosed with Guillain-Barre´ syndrome in 1988. "I had short-term goals and a couple of long-term goals. The short-term goal would be if I was lying in bed and I needed to go to the bathroom, I would see if I could turn over in bed and get up.

"The next goal would be to see if I can get into the bathroom and finish what I had to do. Then the next goal was to get back to bed. In other words, it was just the immediate things, very immediate things, very short-term.

"The long-term goal was to keep from killing myself during the acute phase of the disease, to try and keep from injuring myself severely, because I could have done it so easily. The muscles were just not there; they weren't home."

Ultimately, Kathryn, a retired registered nurse, used a walker and a cane.

"It was very difficult to know at what point I could push myself a little bit," she remembers of that time. "That was one of the problems, I think, when to say I need to just not do anything, or I need to just rest, or I can push myself a little now. It's very hard to make that distinction.

"I avoided doing things that were difficult for me. For instance, I dropped my heating pad. It fell between the bed and the wall, and I reached over to try to get it. I would try to do something like that just once. If it didn't work out, then I just didn't get myself frustrated over it.

"Short-term goals are so important. You can say to yourself, 'The most important thing for me to do right now is to eat my lunch. This is what I have to do now.' I can't emphasize short-term goals enough. And the feeling of being triumphant when you've done that one little thing."

It may be hard to accept that one can truly create, accomplish, and complete big tasks by moving through them in small, easy steps. But it does work. When we bite off more than we can chew, we open ourselves to the possibility of becoming frustrated. For the person with a chronic illness, frustration is always looming around the corner. A whole project, or long-range plans, can go down the tubes. Be sure to set your goals with reachable pause points.

Mary Alice Kerr has learned to do that.

"It's nice to have things to look forward to, without setting yourself up for something you can't do. For example, I have an offer to go skydiving. I want to do that, but I don't know when I'm going to be able to.

"What I didn't do, which I might have done years ago, is say 'Well, I'm going to plan on doing it this Sunday and that's when I'm going to do it,' instead of being tentative about it. So have a goal like that, but don't personally make it something you absolutely have to do, or you're going to be devastated.

"I used to do that: I have to go back to school in a year from now, or I have to be walking at such and such a time. Those might be possibilities, things you would like to do, not somethings you have to do, so you don't get disappointed. Something to look forward to."

A second tactic is to consider a set routine for your days. Physical problems disrupt our lives a great deal. We do not need any more surprises along the way. A routine may seem like a steady and dull way to deal with life, but it needn't be so. Routines, unlike ruts, are general frameworks to help us stay in charge and to tell when things are not going as planned.

Some people arrange their days or weeks so that they have a similar format. They decide the order in which they begin and progress through the day. This way, they can make sure that there are pleasant moments in the morning—to read the paper, sit outside, have a slow cup of coffee.

In the afternoon, a short walk can be built into the routine. Or time to listen to a favorite tape. Or activities that are fun to do after a busy day. The types of activities are limitless.

"I had to decide whether to figure out how to die or

how to live," says Susan Abeyta. "Take classes toward a second master's degree? Make plans for increased financial dependence? Move away from close friends? Do I live as though I'm going to live, or do I live as though I'm going to die?

"I came to the decision that what I'm going to do today is what I want to do today, even if it's something that aims toward a longer term goal."

The exact content of your chosen schedule does not matter. Nor is it a problem if you change it. It is important, though, to figure out your own rhythm and build a life around it. A schedule gets you to take your day seriously and to avoid getting yanked around by the outside world. It may protect you from feelings of chaos, tension, or depression, because you will know what you want to do next in the day, not just what others expect you to do.

Chapter Exercise

Tuning Your Time Lines

1. Think of three short-term goals. They should be relatively routine, not unduly complicated, and well within your ability to do. For example,

   > Cook dinner.
   > Go to the store to shop.
   > Write a letter to your sister.

   Write *your* three goals below:

   1. _____
   2. _____
   3. _____

Now try to break them down into smaller steps, as an efficiency expert would. Reduce each goal to six steps. One way to do this is to assume you are teaching someone how to complete the steps leading to the goal. Every move that is directly related to the ultimate accomplishment must be described. The smaller the bits of behavior, the better. This exercise will help you to think of tasks in a more operational, goal-oriented fashion.

Goal 1—Six steps:

1._____
2. _____
3. _____
4. _____
5. _____
6. _____

Do the same for goals 2 and 3.

2.   Think about some long-term goals you would like to achieve. For example,

—Learn Spanish.

—Learn how to tune-up your engine.

—Get an Associate degree.

Write *your* three goals below.

1. _____
2. _____
3. _____

Now make two time lines for each goal. The first line (Basic Time Line) should encompass a few steps. The second (Detailed Time Line) should include a greater number of steps, with each step smaller than the one before it.

Using Spanish lessons as the example,

Basic Time Line:

▼	▼	▼
Sign up (Sept.)	Mid-Term (Nov.)	Final (Dec.)

Detailed Time Line:

A B C D E F G H I J K L

Steps:

A. Get ideas from friends (July)
B. Get course catalogue (Aug.)
C. Talk to counselor (Aug.)
D. Decide hours (mid-Aug.)
E. Sign up (late Aug.)
F. Get course books (before course begins)

G. Attend first class (early Sept.)
H. Plan study schedule (first week of class)
I. First exam (early Oct.)
J. Treat self to special dessert
K. Meet with study group
L. Final exam (mid-Dec.)

Try to plan your goals in the *most comfortable way.* It is important to remember that this is a task to help you think about how you would like to pace yourself. Process is more important than product for anyone, especially the chronically ill.

If a man does not keep pace with
his companions, perhaps it is because
he hears a distant drummer.

Thoreau

*The person with a chronic illness has a saboteur around
the corner. The urge to make big plans is natural, but
retreat is often necessary. Short-term goals invite success.
Fantasies and excursions from reality can heal. Realistic
goals can be alternated with the balm of imagination.*

Fantasy and imagination are critical to the growing
child's ability to test, revise, accept, and consolidate who
he or she is going to become. Unfortunately, not only do we
reduce the amount of fantasizing as we grow older, but
we are told that grown-ups are not supposed to fantasize
or daydream. The truth is that fantasy and imagination
are useful and acceptable tools for any adult; they are
especially important for people with chronic illness.

A primary goal of fantasy or daydreaming is to uplift
or inspire us. Even negative fantasizing often focuses on
situations in which we "rerun" a scene, hoping for a better
outcome. Perhaps we imagine ourselves at the beach,
with favorite family members. We recall pleasant experiences. Or we create new universes of people and actions
that cannot possibly occur in our real lives. Fantasy is
that self-selected moment when we are alone with our
thoughts, giving ourselves pleasure and calmness or preparing for a future task. It takes us away from the
pressures and pains of the here-and-now.

We are also taught throughout our lives that isolation and being alone are often inappropriate behaviors, perhaps even deviant. And in some instances, that's true. Many theories of psychology emphasize the fundamental importance of interpersonal relations. There is no question that shared human connections are important, indeed indispensable.

Still, many have come to discover that choosing to be alone at selected times is important to their well-being. Solitude is good for you. It is a balm for the mind, body, and soul.

"An inner world of fantasy exists in every human being and finds expression in an infinite variety of different ways," says noted therapist Anthony Storr in his book *Solitude*. He writes, "Whether in young or old, changes of attitude are facilitated by solitude and often by changes of environment as well."

Fantasy and solitude are a powerful pair. Together, they can create the space that heals.

Rebecca Steinberg remembers, "I would awaken at night with the realization, 'Oh, my God, I'm dying.' And I would resurrect my country doctor grandfather and put him in his favorite rocking chair next to my bed, so he was with me all night—very comforting.

"I use visualization to take myself on wonderful journeys to beautiful places and put myself in a healing light and have the light beaming on me. I made up medieval castles and all kinds of things. I've resurrected my parents and put them in the castles so I can visit them when I would go somewhere to heal."

Solitude is useful just by itself, with no accompanying expectations or activities. Time spent alone using your creative faculties is as important as being with others and doing routine things. Both have their place and function; for everything there is a season.

"I don't know how you develop that inner calm that helps you through. I really don't know how that comes about," says Allan Pike. Now 42, Pike underwent a liver transplant at the age of 37. "I've always been sort of a spiritual person, even though I've not been religious. I always felt that I have a lot of inner strength. I don't know how you give that to somebody.

"I think it was a love of life that was a big factor, and the love of little things...the two hours a day that sunlight somehow filtered down this long airshaft into my room buried in this medical complex, the two hours a day when the sun would come in...or the little bird that was on the windowsill. I don't know how you teach people to appreciate those little things."

Mary Alice Kerr, 28, knows the importance of spacing her pleasures without the presence of others. She is likewise aware of the pitfalls.

"Sometimes, I'll just force myself to do something if I'm doing real bad, to do something physical, to get outside, things like that—when I've been at my worst, not being able to get up at all, just having something going on like playing a tape, music, and not just lying there helps—so something is happening."

"Sometimes I rent four movies and spend the day by myself," says Andy Nordstrum, 43, diagnosed with amyotrophic lateral sclerosis, heart disease, and an ulcer. "I like the Cary Grant movies, Alfred Hitchcock, a wide variety. I even like pure schmaltz, like 'It's a Wonderful

Life."'

Some people with chronic illness regulate the pace of their lives and gain perspective by reaching out to others in distress. By absorbing the pain of others, we can re-examine and cauterize our own, calling up the strength we know is there to move on. While it does involve others, the satisfaction is private and deeply felt.

"I love to help people," says Ken Saville. "If someone needs a favor, something where I have to concentrate my energies—if I do that when things get real bad, I feel better. I like to be called upon to do something immediately because somebody *needs* help and is in distress."

Rebecca Steinberg also finds it rewarding to reach out to those who are hurting. She speaks to others with chronic illness.

"I went through all this[cancer], which was agonizing . . . . It's been wonderful to be able to help somebody else, for altruistic reasons, without looking for reward."

Chapter Exercise

Things to Think About

Many people find it difficult to feel comfortable doing solitary activities. What does aloneness mean to you? There are many dimensions to explore. Let's look at some of them. Make notes as you go along.

1. Think of what you do when you are alone and have nothing to do. Are the things you do the same or different than what you did before your illness?

2. What kinds of daydreams or fantasies do you have? Do they involve thoughts and plans about actual activities, or are they more "unreal" and "out-of-this-world"?

3. What are three of the most creative or innovative ideas you have ever had?

4. What are three of the most creative or innovative things you have ever done? Who knows about them?

5. Do your new ideas excite you so much that you have a hard time looking at them calmly?

6. Write about one or two of the most spontaneous things you've ever done. Did you do them alone? With somebody? If so, whom?

7. What activities do you enjoy doing? After you have finished an enjoyable activity, do you tell anyone about the experience? If so, whom?

It is important to try to recapture activities you have enjoyed in the past and which recently you may have discontinued. Review the notes you have just written. Does solitude have a place in your life? In the space that follows, jot down the reasons why it does or does not. Your answers may surprise you. When you have finished reading this book, or the portions you are interested in, come back to what you have written here. Have your feelings changed? If so, note in what way.

79

(Today's Date)

8. Try Something New

There's a time for some things, and a
time for all things; a time for great
things, and a time for small things.
Cervantes

It is easy to stay with the familiar, especially when the vicissitudes of a chronic illness bring uncertainty on a regular basis. However, trying something new, making the uncomfortable comfortable can be a healing and rewarding experience.

We have talked about focusing on small steps and the importance of knowing how to retreat to solitude. Now let's look at those periods when it is important to try something new, to take a risk and become innovative.

Alice Hiat, an artist and long-term cancer survivor, created a sculpture that captures this message well. The artwork is a beautiful, cozy nest surrounded by an encircling wall of slender bundles of reeds. The nest is lined with soft pale wool strands, gently twisted and curled into a soft, touchable cushion.

In the middle of the strands lies the paradoxical form of a stark, dried, and shrunken pomegranate. The pomegranate looks like a dying pod, shriveled and just cracked open. Alice, 55, explained the contrast of the dried pomegranate, a traditional symbol of fertility, with the snug but overprotected nest: "This portrays what happens when your nest becomes a net."

If you become too comfortable in your surroundings, the artist is saying, you may never venture forth and seek new adventures. Exploring, on the other hand, opens you up to the world and keeps you vital and alive. Sometimes the comfortable and familiar transform us from vigorous and productive creatures into desiccated shells unable to grow and flourish.

"I learned to fly," disabled skier John Flanagan states matter-of-factly. "If you want to do it badly enough, you can do it. You should give it a try. It may not be as tough as you think.

"First time I tried a bicycle or a motorcycle, it was always the same thing, wondering if you can do it. In every instance, it was not as tough as I thought it would be."

Emily Masterson, blind and an amputee from diabetes, took the step with help from someone she hadn't even known.

Emily, 44, met a "telephone pal" through the Center for Attitudinal Healing in California, an organization that matches people with similar problems. The goal is to lend support to each other.

"Joe and I clicked right away," Emily, who has a master's degree in special education, recounts. "He was a diabetic who had also lost his sight and he was a sculptor. We shared many of the same ideas about attitude and healing and making the most of our lives.

"He invited me to visit him in Seattle. I had not traveled since 1983 and was afraid to travel alone and visit a strange dialysis unit. Even scarier than my fear of going, however, was my fear of not going and being stuck at home for the rest of my life. As it turned out, there was a very good [dialysis] unit only a few blocks from Joe's apartment, so I made the trip. It was wonderful to walk on the beach with a person I had come to know by telephone and letters."

Chronic illness has a way of making people give up their natural proclivity to try new things. Instead, we find that disabilities frighten people. Often, their cautiousness helps them repress their urge to explore and take risks.

"One of the ways I have avoided loneliness and depression is to participate in activities in my church," says Emily. "I have taken classes and workshops, attended dances, made announcements, and sung in choir performances.

"I remember my son being proud of me when I did the invocation for a Christmas Eve service. It was easy to overcome fear in front of a loving group of people. A couple of years ago, I was invited to join a women's sextet. My voice was nice but nothing outstanding. The music director promised to teach us, so I gave in to a long-held fantasy.

"I reported to the church once a week for voice lessons and twice a week for rehearsals. We selected matching dresses and sang for church services, talent shows, and a conference. We selected the name Touchstone for the sextet, and for almost a year I felt like a mini-celebrity."

If you have a chronic illness, there comes a brief time or period when the illness causes you to focus on your own self-protection. The safety and well-being of your body become the center of your life. This vantage point might be quite appropriate in an acute phase of an illness, but not as a permanent part of your life. "Find something you love,"Sandra McCollum advises, "something you do well and can take pride in. Do something different. I think that's important because so often people with chronic illness aren't valued. We're assumed to be a sort of drain on the system, a drain on human resources. That may be true, but there are many more things we can offer."

Remember some famous people who produced prolifically despite chronic physical problems. Franklin Roosevelt led the nation and vigorously prosecuted a war while confined to a wheelchair following adult-onset polio. Barbara Jordan, the Texas congressperson, served the public well despite confinement to a wheelchair because of neuromuscular disease. John Kennedy campaigned for the presidency and served in that office with often intense chronic pain as a result of a back injury.

Beethoven wrote his final works as his hearing faded and ultimately deserted him. The renowned astrophysicist Stephen Hawking wrote his best-selling *On the Origins of the Universe* while paralyzed by a serious neurologic disease. Elizabeth Browning, bedridden with a back injury, wrote lasting romantic poetry from her sickroom. Florence Nightingale's disabling lung disease didn't stop her from giving advice to the military authorities on how to set up wartime medical services.

Proust wrote his brilliant works under the stress of a disabling respiratory disease. Robert Louis Stevenson gave us the pleasure of his adventure novels written from the confines of his sickbed. Martha Graham, with severe arthritis, brought soaring joy to millions with her innovative dance choreography. Mickey Mantle slugged 536 home runs despite the intense chronic pain and discomfort of injured and battered knees and a leg that doctors thought would eventually have to be amputated (it wasn't).

You must make it your own personal mission to break out of the nests that may be restraining you from trying something new. What is there to try? If not everything, then certainly a great deal, perhaps even something nearby.

For Emily Masterson, an out-of-state trip did the trick. But for you, something closer to home might be more your speed. If you look around the area where you are sitting and reading this book, you will see a number of possible projects you might initiate. A few feet away there may be a TV set or radio that has an attractive program on it that you have not seen or heard.

Around you is furniture that may need refinishing, recovering, or rebuilding. Across the room are walls that can be painted or covered. There may be sculptures to think about, too. (Alice Hiat's powerful work NE(S)T was made without expensive equipment or fancy materials.)

The moral of the story is this: If you open your eyes to the environment, you don't have to go very far (indeed, you may not even have to leave the house) to keep the nest from turning into a net.

Do you have a pet you've been meaning to train? Clothes you want to sew? Books and magazines waiting to be read? An arthritis sufferer we know routinely culls the titles of books she wishes to read (she gets them from newspaper book reviews, the shelves of friends, bookstores, of from browsing through her library's used book sales) and enters them on her home computer spreadsheet. Alongside each entry is a code for fiction, nonfiction, biography, etc. As she reads a book, or sets it aside for later perusal, she checks off each one with another code indicating that it is on her bookshelf.

She says the list eliminates the necessity of keeping in her head the books she "must" read, "should" read, or will read if she happens to come across them.

"It's like my own little library," she says. "It makes me feel rich and secure, but it also is a way for me to know that I can quickly transport myself to another place when I find myself getting stuck with the pain and restrictions of my arthritis. And I have a choice of books to match my mood or distemper."

She disavows any current intention of systematically categorizing the books already in her bookcase. But, she says, the possibility is there.

Lists make good companions in a variety of contexts. Recipes, for one. There are exotic surprises you might try in the kitchen. After all, your stove and refrigerator are basically no different from Julia Child's or the Frugal Gourmet's.

Wonderful music of all kinds is available on the radio or tapes. There are new languages to be learned. Or, get up and go outside. A garden may need to be created. The lawn could stand some fixing up. And what about your neighbor's porch or patio?

Each of us has secret dreams and longings we have carried with us since childhood. While some of us have fulfilled some of them, there are always more to be tried.

Think back to your childhood. Try to remember one thing you wished you could do, or hoped you would do better, when you got older. Remember that wish to be a pianist, a writer, a plumber, a carpenter, a baseball player, a great businessperson, a teacher? Variations and suitable substitutes for all these are still available to bring you joy in some fashion. Resurrect them.

If you are still drawing back, here are some guidelines. Think of different possibilities. To begin, all they require is a little bit of nerve.

Think about your hands. Would you like to carve, build a table, draw, make ceramics, throw a ball, build models, play a musical instrument?

Think about expanding your mind. Would you like to learn about a different country, trace your family lineage, learn about your neighborhood, learn to play chess, investigate the history of your state, understand the stock market?

Think about your creative urges. Everyone can create. Would you like to write, draw, sculpt, photograph, decorate, build, invent?

Think about your social activities. Would you like to meet new people, invite people to your home, start a club, join a volunteer fire department, go out for a beer, have a party, become a volunteer coach, supervise or be a mentor to someone who needs some support?

Think about your body as a whole. Would you like to walk, jog, play tennis, dance, exercise, swim, racewalk, stretch, bicycle, make love?

Chapter Exercise

Make Your Own Adventures

Take a breath. Relax. Now reread the above "Think

abouts," then make a list of 10 activities you always (or almost always) wanted to do but were afraid to try.

1. _____
2. _____
3. _____
4. _____
5. _____
6. _____
7. _____
8. _____
9. _____
10. _____

Look these over and narrow your list to three (more if you are ready to go all out with this new project). You might pick the three that seem the least threatening or provide the greatest challenge. That's up to you.

You can use one of five methods, or all of them.

1. Try to learn all by yourself. This involves trial and error, reading the right material, and practicing privately.

2. You can get an expert to teach you, but you may have to pay or trade for that service. The trade can be something that comes easily for you or involves some skill that you already have, such as babysitting, repairing a broken appliance, running an errand, baking cookies, or helping with some task.

3. Find a class at a local high school, YMCA or YWCA,university, or community college (evening or day). A benefit here is that you will have the camaraderieof other students and the structure of a class to support and pace your learning. You also will have others around to learn from, and if you can control your competitiveness, it can be great fun. Classes are usually not too expensive.

4. Tapes. You can purchase audio- and videotapes for just about any skill. Call your local bookstore, movie rental store, radio, and TV stations.

5. Friends. You might have a friend who is familiar with the area you wish to learn about. See if the friend is willing to help you on an informal basis.

Your personal situation (health, finances, available facilities) will determine which route is best. If you put in a little time each day, your skills will increase. Remember that small steps make the most sense. Expertise is acquired, usually in measurable increments; it is not inborn.

As you look at this whole concept, you may find that an internal dialogue again emerges to stop you. Let's listen.

1. "I have no talent." You don't need talent to reach moderate proficiency in almost any area—just persistence. If you begin to be a perfectionist, you are

building a new kind of prison-nest to stop you from exploring.

2. "People will laugh at me." People won't laugh at you. Everyone (whether you are told or not) has secret, unfulfilled dreams. If they see you are serious about your goal, they may even be inspired to imitate you.

3. "It takes too long." Time goes by whether we try new things or sit still. We all have read about the 85-year-old grandmother who gets her college degree. The last days, weeks, and years of your life have probably passed more quickly than you had expected. So what if it takes time? Time passes. Use it.

4. "What if I stop in the middle?" Again, so what? It's your business. You are not in elementary school, and your parents or spouses are not in charge. This is not a test. It's an experiment, and you are in control. In any case, even if you do stop early, you have learned something—even if it's only that you don't care to pursue the activity you started.

5. "I won't be as good as I hoped I'd be." Try to remember the sculpture of the dried-out pomegranate. Only inactivity is truly depressing. Lower your expectations of yourself. Remember: *Accepting a new challenge at a new level of competence takes courage.*

Perhaps you are not as good as you would have liked to be or had expected to be. Trying makes you stronger, and you can never be certain how you will progress.

6. "I'm scared and new things make me anxious." That is a normal reaction. Anxiety is another experience to master. You may not be able to change what is chronic, but it's worth giving a good shot at reducing your anxiety.

7. "I don't know how to start." There are resources for new activities and innovative ideas in a variety of newspapers and magazines. There are courses described in the catalogues of the YMCA and similar community associations. Read the bulletin boards at local religious organizations, hobby shops, libraries, and your place of employment. Check the listings in the telephone Yellow Pages under associations and organizations. Ask people (not family members) how they stay mentally and emotionally youthful. Pretend you are younger—what would you do to fill your time?

Finally, bear in mind that we are creatures of habit. We tend to get into ruts. There are very simple things you can do in your daily routine to feel adventuresome. For example, drive or walk to the store using a new route. Try a new cereal for breakfast (goodness knows, there are enough of them to choose from). Cook or prepare something different for dinner tonight.

Get a new hairstyle. Try new frames for your eyeglasses. Buy clothing that projects a new image (you can always change back). Call somebody you have wanted to call, but haven't.

Rearrange your furniture (or get someone to help you). If your room or house is too tidy, mess it up and see how it feels. If it's always messy, straighten it up and see how that feels.

The trick of all the exercises is to begin to think of yourself as someone who is open, not closed, to new experiences. Alice Hiat's nest is a reminder to us all to get out of our comfortable ruts and try something new.

Allan Pike, physician and former patient, supports that outlook:

"Do something every day that's fun and that you enjoy," he suggests, "even if you're sick, whether it's reading a book or eating ice cream. Focus on the pleasures. Focus on your family. Enjoy the people around you.

"If you die...who knows? That may be the end. Really try to take each day at a time and not worry about what might happen."

In the end, it may be useful to recall Auntie Mame, that frenetic purveyor of a certain charm and good cheer. "The world is a feast," she declared, "and most poor suckers are starving to death."

It's your turn. Take a (new) bite.

9. Don't Forget Your Daily Shots — of Inspiration

Oh, every year hath its winter,
And every year hath its rain—
But a day is always coming
When the birds go north again.
Ella Higginson

We all have our own private lists of experiences that renew and inspire us. We can order up a shot of inspiration in music, art, sports, family life. We must seek out these "shots" aggressively and assertively. Context-setting is important. So is learning how to integrate inspiration into daily routine.

Can you recall those days long ago when, as a child, you wandered into a local movie theater and sat down in the darkness in quickening anticipation of watching the cinematic magic unfold? You probably had a box of popcorn in your hand and perhaps a good friend sitting next to you.

The curtain opened, and after the coming attractions were screened, the main feature began. Suddenly, an amazing experience began to transpire. The larger-than-life hero or heroine slowly began to capture your undivided attention, your gut and your heart.

You followed the story, your eyes and ears riveted to the screen. The plot felt as if it had been made for you. The characters were alive and their dilemmas real. Gradually, you found yourself psychologically merged with the protagonist.

As you watched each scene, you experienced a wide range of emotions, including anxiety, excitement, fear, joy, sorrow, and perhaps at the end, relief.

As the lights came up, you felt transformed. You were not the same person who had entered the theater a few hours earlier. As you left the building and faced the harshness of daylight, you were filled with confusing thoughts and feelings.

Part of this was the sense of unreality; you knew what you had just seen was "only a story." But it seemed so real. In fact, it seemed more real than the street and cars now in front of you. It may have been impossible to talk about your reactions beyond telling others it was "great," or "cool," or "heavy."

The popular terms could not capture how profoundly you were touched. Somehow, you really had gone through a change; somehow, your emotions really were moved. The main character in the movie altered your walk and modified your style of speaking. You even looked at dinner that night, a fight with your sister, and your classmates and teachers with new eyes. A new aspect of your personality was inspired by that film.

The experience of inspiration seems somehow mysterious. It happens to us when we least expect it. Fortunately, it happens sometimes when we need it most. When it does happen, our daily routine takes on new meaning and we are, indeed, transformed.

"I became attentive to the little pleasures," Allan Pike recalls of the period immediately following his liver transplant, "enjoying a meal, being read to, enjoying a little walk, eating ice cream. It was almost like I was trying to suck everything pleasurable out of the experiences that I had while I was there.

"I remember I got a pass one day to leave the hospital for six hours. I went to a local park...and lay down. There were a lot of college kids there—a big grassy hill, it was a beautiful summer day—and I just tried to soak in the beauty of nature around me, and just appreciated being there, just trying to focus on happiness and being alive, even though I was in pain and not sure if I was in the middle of rejection of my liver transplant."

There are those who assume that inspiration is impossible to program. Great writers, actors, coaches, religious leaders, singers, and musicians all know that often inspiration can be encouraged and effective in many situations. We may not be able to predict how to inspire greatness. But we can inspire deep feelings and personal reactions.

We are fortunate. We have experienced situations in our lives that, with remarkable predictability, do lift our spirits. When we remember or re-experience them, they cause our hearts to fill and our heads to sing in pleasurable recognition. Our own personal history is a powerful and available resource, ready to be tapped for inspirational needs.

Listen to Sandra McCollum:

"When I was in school, I wasn't allowed to take physical education because of my asthma. I grew up in a neighborhood full of boys; I was the only girl. I remember once coming home because I couldn't take gym, and I was crying, and then I got mad.

"There was a baseball game going on in the lot a block from our house, and so I asked my mother and went out and played baseball. It was amazing. The kids who knew me on the block were more accepting of me and pretty protective.

"I had a pretty good arm and I could throw, so I played first base because I didn't have to run. I could stand on the base. Then we worked out a deal where, when I would bat, if I didn't strike out or hit a home run, somebody would run for me. It was wonderful.

"We got a TV pretty early and I would see many sports heroes who played when they were hurt, and overcame their injuries—Wilma Rudolph had polio and won an Olympic gold medal. She was just this extraordinary hero to me. So sports for me was really important to watch, to be a part of it when I could.

"Playing baseball, I sort of laughed because it was a lot more fun than being in the smelly gym wearing those awful little blue gym suits that nobody looks good in."

We find that many people struggling with chronic illness need shots of inspiration to deal with the hard work of getting through each day when they do not feel well. It is energizing and emotionally satisfying to learn and relearn the behaviors that put you in contact with the wellsprings of your spiritual self.

People tell us over and over again that they will listen to a special piece of music, read a passage from a book, look at the sky on a starry night, smell a night-time smell, and suddenly they feel they have renewed energy.

When Allan Pike was in the hospital recuperating from his operation, he decided to make a list of things to do when he got better. While he ruefully reports that he hasn't adhered faithfully to that promise, one item on his list remains important.

"I said I'd listen to more music. In the hospital, it was useful. I never had time [before] to just listen—not just in the background. It kinda raised my spirits—the Moody Blues was one group I liked. I was still thinking about being sick, but it made me think good thoughts. Nothing too cerebral. Music with lyrics, upbeat lyrics, happy songs. They were the best."

Rebecca Steinberg reports, "Music has always played an important part in my life. I resurrected old songs and made up new, sort of hymn-like chants, and brought music in to help me through the whole thing. And it did. Music with personal words that involved healing made a difference in helping me find my center again."

Carlos Diaz, 40, fills his days with music in a way to fit his moods. Diaz, who is severely learning disabled, is a very successful small business owner.

"Sad music makes me think about my life," he explains. "At work, I plan the day using different music in the morning, in the afternoon, and later in the day. I start the day with classical music. As the day goes on, I change to popular music, to a station with modern songs to give me energy. It makes the day go nicely."

Often, those we interviewed spoke movingly of how the struggles with their own illness inspired them. They did not see that as a paradox.

"I'm almost happy that I went through all this, it's weird," Allan Pike asserts. "I would not give it up. I had so many good experiences that I felt changed me for the better. If someone said, 'You could be totally healthy and back where you were in 1985,' I wouldn't take it because I feel I got something very positive out of the experience.

"The things I remember are the good things, the positive stuff. Keeping myself aware of my illness actually is a good thing because it made me appreciate what I had. So maybe this is God's way of gently reminding me that I'm mortal.

"I had sort of gotten back in a rut...starting to worry about little diddly things. The last few weeks and months I've been focused more on my illness and trying to remember the lessons I learned."

Mary Alice Kerr concurs:

"If I had the choice, I would choose the same path again. I feel I have benefitted from my circumstances. I know I'm not being ignored. I have closer friendships and have experienced more tenderness than ever before."

Inspiration seems to move us from our body boundaries and our immediate concerns to a bigger picture. It gives us perspective and taps our more hope-filled, universal consciousness. Perhaps this is why some works of art, music, literature, and history are known as classic. They seem to touch people and to inspire over many generations.

It is probably no coincidence that the vast majority of Oscar-winning films and films nominated for an Academy Award over the past half-century have grand themes of inspiration. Go see them for yourself. To get you started, the following lists three award winners or nominees from each decade since 1930.

- 1930-1939
  All Quiet on the Western Front
  The Champ
  Gone With the Wind

- 1940-1949
  How Green Was My Valley
  Gentleman's Agreement
  The Best Years of Our Lives

- 1950-1959
  The African Queen
  High Noon
  On the Waterfront

- 1960-1969
  To Kill a Mockingbird
  Lilies of the Field
  A Man for All Seasons

- 1970-1979
  Man of La Mancha
  Annie Hall
  Julia

- 1980-1989
  Chariots of Fire
  Field of Dreams
  Empire of the Sun

- 1990-
  Dances with Wolves

Inspiration also means renewing the strengths and abilities that helped to define you before your illness or disability. Retrieving the moment of a past pleasure may mean reaching back internally for something that has diminished or been set aside. It is a good feeling, and mentally healthy, to be able to relink the connection between your present self and your past, perhaps more fully functioning, self.

"I continued to draw after my accident," recalls artist Beth Salazar. Salazar, 45, an active runner who taught and studied karate, developed arthritis as a result of injuries sustained in a car crash. "I needed to do something that said I was normal. Not running was a major depressant. I had run every day for 10 years. I kept trying to run, but it hurt.

"I could draw and walk and I also tried to play the guitar. I took my cast off and made my fingers move in a chord position, then I made them move to the strings. It was a step-by-step process."

Going to her old karate class also proved to be important. "It was helpful to do normal things and watch people moving. I didn't realize how much I had invested in my physical sense of self or how much my self-worth was measured by what I had done physically."

Chapter Exercise

Inspiration Energizer Chart

One of the tasks of someone with a chronic illness is to learn how to get energized from old and new sources. One source of energy can come from past inspirational experiences—sometimes long forgotten. With practice, you can learn to actively use and plan inspirational events in your daily life. We will show you how.

Exercise 1 - Remembering When . . .

Begin by making a list of inspiring life circumstances. They may overlap or they may be less than absolutely clear in your mind. Don't worry about that. The point is to help you recapture a mood, a feeling, an emotional uplift you may have forgotten or ignored for too long. It is always useful to reenter the reservoir of memories we all carry around and recapture the joys and good times of the past.

First, find a quiet, familiar setting where you can be alone with your own thoughts and have no interruptions. Make yourself comfortable. For example, lower the lights, keep some refreshments at your side, make sure you have pencil and paper and something to write or lean on. It is important to keep in mind that, like some of the other tasks outlined in this handbook, this exercise will not be easy. It requires patience and practice. But, our experience tells us, you can do it.

It is important to remember that these tasks are not a formula for so-called peak experiences. They are instead pathways to help you explore how to create situations that lift you from the confines of distress and into more comfortable and energetic states of mind. That is the inspiration we are talking about.

There are two ways to proceed. You may want to try one instead of the other, or do both. We suggest you start with the first. However you begin, first take a minute to relax. Try to bring back the feelings they evoked as you look them over.

1.   Focusing on your own experiences, list the events
     in your life that you remember having inspired
     you—those events, big and small, that filled you
     with fresh energy and new resolve. Be as specific
     and explanatory as you wish. As the memories
     return, you may find yourself writing more details
     than you have remembered in a long time. Let
     your mind relax; try to picture the remembered
     scene or events.

2.   To help you get a more defined sense of your
     growth and inspirational experiences, try the
     following: Take your age (to the nearest upper

year) and divide it into five parts. For example, if you are 50 years old, you will have five, equally spaced age segments (0-10, 10-20, etc.). Then, try to remember at least two inspirational events for each age category. Of course, you will recall more recent events more readily. You might want to ask relatives and friends for help in recalling earlier inspirational experiences. Going through your family album could be a good way to start.

Exercise 2 - Inspirational Sentence Completion

To make sure you haven't missed any, fill in the following incomplete sentences.

1. I sure wish I could again experience _____

_____

2. I felt great some time ago, when I _____

_____

3. I often remember the amazing moment when I _____

_____

4. I can't forget the one time that I _____

_____

5. I felt I accomplished something important when I _____

_____

6. I felt changed the moment when _____

_____

7. I was inspired the time when _____

_____

8. I gained a new perspective when _____

9. I felt transformed when _____

10. A remarkable moment in my life was when _____

Exercise 3 - Identify the Ingredients

Why are these experiences important to you? What about them makes you remember them? One way to answer those questions is to think about what each of the experiences had in common.

1. Did they involve people or a person?
2. Did they involve esthetic beauty?
3. Did they involve solving a problem or a similar mental activity?
4. Did they involve music?
5. Did they involve watching some performance or show?
6. Did they involve travel or a vacation?
7. Did they involve sharing an important experience?
8. Did they take place outdoors?
9. Were they "alone" experiences, without anyone else present?
10. Were they religious experiences?
11. What other commonalities were there?

Exercise 4 - Shots of Inspiration

As you probably have noticed when doing the above tasks, some inspirational events involved passive activity on your part (e.g., listening, enjoying a happy moment with friends), while others required more active involvement (e.g., sports participation, arranging a family outing). The important message is: what inspired you before will inspire you again. Here's how.

Listed below are some inspiration shots and examples of the kind of involvement each may require—receptive, intermediate, active. Look over our examples carefully. Now get a blank piece of paper and prepare your own chart using the headings in the example.

Exercise 5 - Inspiration Energizer Chart

Inspiration Shots	Receptive	Intermediate	Active
Accomplishment	Read a book about Magic Johnson	Make a model	Build a bookcase
Ceremonial	Watch a flag raising	Participate in a parade	Be inducted into a group
Sports	Watch a ball game on TV	Watch a game at a local field or stadium	Play catch or join a team as friend, coach, booster
Friendship	Re-read old letters; look at old photos	Write a letter; make a phone call	Make a visit; have lunch with a friend

With the knowledge gained from the above, you can now create your own personal and private Inspiration Energizer Chart. We have provided a guide to enable you to do it on a daily basis.

Step 1. Every morning, plan your shot of inspiration for the day, using the Inspiration Energizer Chart below.

Step 2. Every evening, after the shot of inspiration has occurred, indicate, with the appropriate number from the accompanying "Did It Help?" list on page 106, how much it helped you emotionally or if the planned shot didn't occur at all.

Step 3. Repeat the procedure for each day of the week.

Inspiration Energizer Chart

Inspiration Shot Planned	*Did It Help?*
Monday_____	_____
_____	_____
Tuesday _____	_____
_____	_____
Wednesday _____	_____
_____	_____
Thursday _____	_____
_____	_____
Friday _____	_____
_____	_____
Saturday _____	_____
_____	_____
Sunday _____	_____
_____	_____

Did It Help?

1—Not at all
2—Minimally
3—Yes and no
4—Somewhat
5—Very much
6—"Shot" didn't occur

Step 4. Keep a folder for these charts and assess progress and changes over one-month, three-month, and six-month periods. Some people find it easier to use note cards instead of a folder.

There are some remedies
worse than the disease.
**Publilius Syrus
(Maxim 301)**

The chronic sufferer must learn to cope with advice-givers and poultice-bearers. It helps to have in place an early-warning alert system designed to help you avoid too much advice that can ruin even the best of days. It is important to understand the ever-present vulnerability to advice and the accompanying longing for cures. Identifying people, places, and times that are intrusive can help you to avoid the next confrontation.

Most chronic sufferers have friends and family who are sensitive and concerned about the sufferer's discomfort. Often, however, they are not sure of how to help the patient feel better, and their lack of knowledge makes them feel awkward.

In addition, motivation for offering advice can range from genuinely caring to camouflaged anger to inadvertent insensitivity. Advice-givers often do not know what is calming or appropriate without asking the sufferer first.

For one person, soft, quiet words are helpful. For some, an hour or two of solitude is calming. For still others, suggestions regarding diet or exercise can be helpful. Some feel better listening to friends talk about themselves and their daily activities. Some are soothed by making plans about the future, while others feel threatened and are angered by the same conversation.

It is crucial, therefore, that the person with a chronic illness let caring others know what is comfortable, in what doses and at what times. This is not always an easy task, as Rebecca Steinberg reports.

"I was told by the nurse, 'Now go ahead and have a good cry.'

"I said, 'What do you mean, have a good cry? I don't want to have a good cry.'

"She said, 'Well, what are you going to do?' I said, 'I'm going to call my friends who have had mastectomies and ask them some questions. I don't feel like crying. I feel like getting the information that I need to know.'

"For her to come in there and assume that I was ready to cry all night, was infuriating. I mean, I was a perfect stranger to her and she was being presumptuous to think that my initial reaction was going to be to cry. It made me mad."

"It's nice to have help," asserts Mary Alice Kerr, "but there's a difference between people trying to help and people taking over."

People who offer "cures" often have their own agendas, either acknowledged or unacknowledged. Some of these are:

1. Profit-making. "If she buys my magic-making pills, I will make a lot of money."

2. Power trip. "If he does what I say, I'll have influence over him."

3. Forced intimacy. "This worked for me, so I want to share it with you."

4. Casually manipulative. "I have the answer; you don't."

5. Provocative and exciting. "This amazing cure will knock your socks off."

6. Judgmental. "People who don't listen to me are idiots."

7. Punitive and sadistic. "I suffered; you'll suffer—so here's one of the ways you can suffer as I did."

8. Guilt-producing. "I care so much for you, why don't you do what I tell you?"

"Healthy people argued to assure me that I got sick because I was angry," asserts Carol Borneo, diagnosed with cancer. "Other people make us feel like cretins. I say, 'How dare you say you know better than me? Don't tell me about cures.' You wonder when it doesn't work, how your self-esteem goes down when you find your cancer's not leaving.

"I have to do what I do. I know what's going on inside me. I've done everything that's best for me in dealing with what I'm given."

Chapter Exercises

Personal Avoidance List (PAL)

"Cures" can be interesting and motivating sources of learning. They can provide social opportunities. Or, as is the target of these exercises, they can be large, exhausting energy drains. The following is a practical approach for learning how to control your own reactions to, and interpretations of, what others present to you. Keep in mind that the goal is to liberate you from wasting time and energy and to put you in charge of your life.

What follows is a self-help guide to issues to consider when you are faced with a new "cure." Remember: As this chapter has emphasized, you do not have to do everything suggested here. Use as many or as few of these suggestions as you feel comfortable using.

1. Knowing Your Moods

Moods can be understood on a continuum—from *needy* to *neutral* to *angry*. They can be thought about as questions and they can change from time to time. You need to know where you are on the continuum when faced with a "cure."

a. **Needy.** Are you in a longing, depressed mood in which the lure of instant cures or quick remedies takes hold in your mind and becomes a constant focus of your attention? In this context, each offered "cure" is a potential and energetic offer of hope leading to possible despair.

b. **Objective.** Are you feeling emotionally balanced, at

equilibrium with your problems, so that you are able to evaluate the possible and probable long-term outcomes? Unsolicited "cures" are interesting, curious, and intriguing, but they are not the ultimate answer.

c.   **Angry.** Are you feeling angry and resentful about all cures, all hope of recovery, all givers of ideas? Have you recently been injured or disappointed by a "cure" or "curegiver"? When you are frustrated and angry, you are at high risk for stress when things do not go as planned.

2. Knowing Your "Cure" History
Many approaches and ideas can be offered as "cures." Here are some of them:

medicine	exercises
group support	acupuncture
astrology	special foods and diets
psychotherapy	crystal healing
living a clean life	vitamins
prayer	meditation

Think about whether you have been involved with and emotionally interested in "cures" that are different from what your doctor, or other health professionals, have recommended. Describe three examples. Then answer the accompanying questions for each of the three.

"Cure" Examples

1.

2.

3.

a.   Who recommended it?
     What was that person's motivation?
     Where were you on the mood continuum?
     What intrigued you about it?
     How much did it cost?
     How long did you stick with it?
     If it helped, how?
     Did it do damage?
     If so, what kind of damage?

b.   Who recommended it?
     What was that person's motivation?
     Where were you on the mood continuum?
     What intrigued you about it?
     How much did it cost?
     How long did you stick with it?
     If it helped, how?
     Did it do damage?
     If so, what kind of damage?

c.   Who recommended it?

What was that person's motivation?

Where were you on the mood continuum?

What intrigued you about it?

How much did it cost?

How long did you stick with it?

If it helped, how?

Did it do damage?

If so, what kind?

3. Knowing About Emotional Waste

It is important to consider the possibility of what we call emotional waste when a "cure" is offered. The following waste basket questions will help you to assess that possibility:

a.   Can I emotionally afford to listen and get curious?

b.   What is the likelihood that I will waste my time or energy with anger misdirected at myself for past failed attempts or money wasted?

c.   What is the likelihood that I will waste my time or energy because of someone who is offering the impossible?

d.   What is the likelihood that I will waste my time or energy on others who try things foolishly?

4. Knowing How to Do a Quick-Check Anti-Victim Alert

When a "cure" opportunity presents itself, ask yourself the following questions:

a.   Where am I on my mood continuum? Mark the spot below.

Needy . . . . Objective . . . . .Angry

b.   What is the motivation of the person offering me a "cure?"

c.   Can I emotionally afford to listen and get curious?

d.   What has happened with similar "cures" in the past?

5. Knowing How to Use a "Cure Diary"

To keep track of responses to advice on an ongoing basis, create a "cure diary."

a.   Note the sequence of events around "cures," including your reactions.

b.   Note how you have used experts to evaluate the "cure."

c.   Note how you have shared your experience with others.

d.   Note what you read about "cures" in magazines and newspapers.

e.   Note ways you waste time and energy involving yourself with "cures."

6. Knowing How to Detach

Some sufferers cannot say "no" to those offering new "cures." They feel obligated to agree to consider something and report back. To help detach yourself from unwanted and unsolicited obligations, begin to practice the art of listening (when you choose to listen). Take down a note or two in a little notebook or on a note card and tell the "cure" bringer that you will think about it. Then, when you feel ready to respond, you can do so—at your own chosen pace, level of independent information about the recommended "cure," and emotional readiness. It is in your control. Don't be stampeded. Learning how not to feel obligated by a suggestion is a critical skill.

It is also good to keep track of these "cure" suggestions. Begin to create a personal list of people and "cures" that have been stressful—your Personal Avoidance List, or PAL. Watch these closely. It makes for an interesting section in your "Cure Diary" and keeps you listening and observing.

11. You Be the Judge

Better put a strong fence 'round the top of the cliff,
than an ambulance down in the valley.
Joseph Malines

*Physical stress will often decrease your ability to think and
judge correctly, sometimes at a critical period. The more
you hurt, the more you experience depression and anxiety,
resulting in a lowered ability to think clearly and judge
situations well. There are ways to acquire judgment.*

When faced with erratic cycles of pain or incessant physical struggles, you need all the good judgment you can muster. You need to be clear-sighted and thoughtful to protect yourself from pain, injury, or further illness. You need to judge accurately the danger of new situations and know when to approach and when to back away.

You need to know how to use interpersonal cues. For example, how do you clearly signal for help when your spouse or companion has missed the fact that you were struggling with joint pain due to arthritis? The dilemma is that just when you reach the maximum level of efficiency, you often find yourself frustrated, overwhelmed, and confused. You have the least, not the greatest, degree of good judgment available.

All judgment is learned; it is not innate. When infants are born, they have no judgment. How do we know? When they are hungry, they cry. When they are tired, they cry. When they are uncomfortable, they cry. They are unable to solve problems. They cry and must rely on the good judgment of their caretaker.

A 1 year old plays with fascination with a plug in an

electrical socket. A 3 year old yanks a dog across the room by its ears and looks surprised when the animal angrily snaps. A 5 year old darts across the street to chase after an errant ball. The child cannot judge the danger of her innocent behavior.

Clearly, your judgment skills have taken years to develop. You have learned through

— messages from your parents
— observations of cause and effect (the concept of cause and effect is not firmly and completely established in children until about age 11 or 12)
— your own trial-and-error attempts to deal with the world
— your reasoning skills.

Good judgment is hard to come by, and yet as a person approaches adulthood, judgment operates with intricate ease. You have learned to size up danger from both the inside (your body) and outside (the physical world). And you have learned that, to take care of yourself, you must read the cues of those around you—whether friend or foe—and plan a strategy to cope with the situation.

Even with the best judgment and preparation, Sandra McCollum has learned, strategies sometimes need to be altered suddenly and without warning—for example, when medication she brought along on a trip didn't work.

"We went to Hawaii and I got really sick and I had to come home. I think it was a combination of a long plane ride, and those planes just don't have enough air.

"At first we tried to decide whether to go to the hospital in Hawaii or make this incredible trip back. I really knew I was in trouble, so I picked up the phone and called the biggest health-care place there and talked to one of the doctors.

"I tried to tell him a little about my history and what I was going through, and some of the regime. He cut me off totally. He said, 'Madam, Hawaii is the best place in the world to live and so the best doctors in the world are here.'

"And I though, 'Oh, God.' And he said, 'We use only the most up-to-date treatments and we have absolutely everything here and whatever you brought with you we probably don't need to see.'

"I asked him about an air ambulance [to the hospital] and he said an air ambulance won't even touch you until you're stabilized because you're flying over the water and you can't land. So I hung up the phone and went in and combed my hair and I put my lipstick on and I said [to my husband], 'Let's go home.'

"I look back and we planned this trip to Hawaii for months and it was really discouraging to me because then you feel like you failed and feel guilty. And I thought, 'But gosh, there's all these places we can go that are closer.' And it made me realize it's not smart to sort of have this one thing that you plan for without having a back-up.

"I learned that it's not smart to take a trip where I need to be in a plane more than a couple of hours. Maybe another thing to think about is always have a plan B. You know, when you put all your eggs in one basket . . . ."

Chronic stress interferes with familiar and predictable routines. An erratic pattern of coping is observed in people who are normally reasonable about monitoring their need for sleep, food, and exercise. They tend to lose their good judgment when they are under the weather.

Someone who ordinarily might plan his day carefully finds that when he is sick, he becomes impulsive, overreactive, or timid in dealing with his time and responsibilities. People who are usually socially receptive and considerate become aggressive, tearful, or withdrawn when they feel sick.

The athletic male who has taken excellent care of his body by working out regularly suddenly experiences pain from a lower back injury. He responds by trying to ignore the discomfort and by working out for two hours instead of his usual 45 minutes and running eight miles instead of his usual four. Why does he do this? Perhaps to prove to himself that he is not vulnerable.

The diabetic is caught in the excitement of a vacation trip. She ignores normal dietary caution and finds herself in a bind. The high sugar content of careless food choices makes her shaky. She needs insulin. She does not take time to read her sugar level, but estimates the dose of insulin required to antidote the sugar. She takes too much and feels the impact of insulin shock.

The heart patient experiences some chest pain while carrying out the third load of garbage. In response, he retreats and calls in sick to work. With fear and trepidation, he crawls into bed, expecting the worse.

The woman with a history of ulcers plans to go out to celebrate her new promotion with friends. She has a very carefully prescribed diet. Her friends want Mexican food. She goes along and eats because she does not want to say no. She suffers as a result.

These are not unusual events. The examples are

numerous. When people do not exercise good judgment, they tend to deny problems and further stress themselves. Cues are ambivalent, mixed, and uncertain.

What is important to emphasize here is that you are the best informant about what is happening in your body. After all, it's been with you since the beginning. Your body requires a wise and careful director. You have to be both mother and father, therapist and coach; both the enthusiastic fan and the angel of mercy who knows when to say it's time to rest and relax. You must know what it needs.

Interestingly, you are probably doing this most of the time without even thinking about it. When it doesn't go on automatically, it may require a mental kick, a psychological jump-start. To do that, you have to pay attention to when you are thinking clearly and operating as your own best friend.

Just as any serious athlete is aware, you have to prepare yourself for the potential effects of physical exertion. Long-distance runners have known for years, for example, to expect to confront the phenomenon known as "the wall." It is a fierce resistance, experienced almost as a literal presence, that defeats the will to continue. The best, and the determined, go on.

"I took precautions to treat myself in advance before going out," Neil Bischkoff remembers about the period after he was diagnosed with asthma. He was somewhat surprised, then, when he started skiing 10 years later, to find that "even with premedicating myself I still would have acute asthmatic bronchospasms. There were times when I would find myself out skiing having bronchospasms. The first time, I didn't know what was happening because

I've always been alert to things in my body.

"After the first experience—it was a stunner—I expected it. If I know it will happen, I don't panic. I believe in my body. I have faith that my body will work. For years thereafter, it would be the same thing. I'd hit the wall after 15 minutes of exercise in the cold air. Cross-country skiing is very demanding on the heart and lungs.

"I would give myself a chance to recover and I would be out again. I'd send off the people with me, usually my wife. She's not an alarmist. She trusted me, too. I hyperventilated for 15 to 30 minutes. I'd recover slowly and wait until it was all done. Then I'd resume.

"I just don't push through when I hit the wall. I wait and the wall dissipates."

Neil also has made judgments about the limits of his bicycle riding, learning that breathing problems happen "less frequently" if he does not go uphill. The same sense of precaution holds true about running to make a plane at the airport. "Just try to get there early," he advises.

Let this be your first task. Think of 10 situations in which you did not protect your body with your best judgment. What was the situation? What did you do? What were the consequences? Write about them in the following blank spaces.

1. _____
2. _____
3. _____
4. _____
5. _____
6. _____
7. _____

8. _____

9. _____

10. _____

Now, look over each example of impulsive or careless judgment or overcautious judgment. Try to analyze the pattern. Are you someone who ignores or *denies* physical cues, overreacts by *defying* them, *retreats* needlessly to inactivity when you feel uneasy, or *relies* on others by passing decision-making on to those around you? Do you fall apart, *regress* and have tantrums?

Do you

DENY?

DEFY?

RETREAT?

RELY?

REGRESS?

Or do you display a combination of these? Don't think this over casually. Don't just look at the moment when you are experiencing a physical symptom. Think of what you do a few hours later or a day later. Sometimes we use poor judgment and it simmers like a stew.

Rachel Crawford is a 46-year-old woman with serious arthritis. She wakes up Saturday morning with aches and pains after a period of relative comfort. The pain threatens her plans for the day. She fears that she will not be able to go grocery shopping with her friend, and she finds it difficult to make breakfast and get dressed.

She takes her medication. She is slowly getting

angry, and she moves deliberately and carefully. She copes well and gets through each event with determination. She eats and dresses, but it takes an extra 30 minutes.

So far, so good. She meets her friend and tells her about her discomfort, so they walk slowly and spend less time shopping than planned. She will just have to do without some food items. Until now, Rachel sounds completely in charge—but then the simmer in the pot turns to a boil.

Two days later the pain has decreased, but not disappeared. She is furious. She "forgets" to take her normal dose of medicine. The poor judgment has taken its toll later than expected. Within hours she is in great pain and feels like a victim—again.

Medicines further complicate the picture. Sometimes the side effects are disruptive and cause a whole new array of symptoms to emerge (see Chapter 19): irritability, intestinal problems, shakiness, sleeping difficulty, bloating, dry mouth. All are an unintended part of the treatment regime. Consider if any of these, or others, have upset and altered the way you use judgment to properly medicate yourself.

Consider, too, what your judgment ability does to others around you. People who ignore symptoms find themselves collapsed and helpless after the denial wears off. The person who acts out in rebellion against signs and cues also folds up, and friends and family have to take over and cover wounded pride or contend with other consequences.

The person who retreats too quickly becomes regressed and childlike. The person who lets others take over when feeling bad is inviting self-resentment about having adults take on parenting roles with each other.

As you can see, judgment not only involves you and your well-being. It also affects the people who are near and dear to you. You have a responsibility to protect them as well. As adults we know that it is important to share decision-making with people who are affected by the decisions. If you do not heed the impact of your behavior on others, there is a high risk for bad feelings, confusion, and miscommunication.

Jim O'Connor has emphysema. If his poor judgment results in his going to a party with his friends and drinking too much, what will happen? As he becomes tipsy, his friends will have to worry silently about his well-being. He may require help to get home. His labored breathing may frighten and concern them. His friends may even feel guilty over his getting into a medically threatening state. He has obviously placed a serious burden on them.

Maria Conti has a heart condition. She has important dietary restrictions that protect her cardiac functions. This night she sits down at the dinner table with her husband and pours salt profusely on her potatoes. They go to sleep, and she awakens during the night with swelling and discomfort.

Her husband wakes up, too, and worries about her health. He stays up with her and loses two hours of sleep. He has a hard time getting started in the morning and is sluggish going to work. He feels worried, tired, frustrated, and a little annoyed. Maria's behavior has affected both lives.

Sometimes there is truly nothing you can do about the variations in physical problems. Medical reality, not judgment, is the factor. When that is the case, there is no reason to be anxiously self-critical—to compound the problem with scathing thoughts of "I should have. . . ."

Punishment is not the goal. Your illness or disability is an unfair blow against you. But judgment is a way of recognizing that circumstance and acting reasonably in response. It is one human skill that separates us from animals. When they are injured or neglected, they cannot plan new coping strategies. We can. Judgment may not cure you, but it can protect you from further damage and allow you to control things.

What if you know that your judgment deteriorates, but you cannot alter it? The pain and discomfort are overwhelming and you tend to overreact. What then? We suggest you seek assistance. Get professional help from someone who has dealt with illness—your doctor, the nurse, physical therapist, occupational therapist, counselor, psychologist, social worker, psychiatrist, clergyperson, coach.

Perhaps you still feel this has nothing to do with you. Maybe you are not sure whether this happens. There's an easy way to check. Just ask those who are close to you. Your spouse, your companion or friend, your colleagues all know how you change. If they trust that you can handle feedback, they will tell you something about yourself. It's a good idea to check on your judgment soon, since in the end, you will have to put it to use.

Chapter Exercise

Judging Your Judgment

It takes time and observation to figure out if there are connections between what you do and what your body experiences. The focus should always be toward the future. To repair and improve coping is the best strategy you can employ. This message is not meant to provoke shame and self-doubt, but to elicit constructive "scientific" self-observation and introspective self-awareness.

Along these lines, stay on the alert for situations that tend to load the dice in a destructive fashion. Consider some of the following. These are times when you may be most emotional and least able to keep a perspective. Go over them carefully and underline the relevant examples in each. If no example fits your experience in a particular category, add your own. Next to each, note the day of the week when you most recently had that experience within the last month. Describe what happened:

1. When you were frustrated by events out of your control (at work or home, the weather, traffic, a stubbed toe, etc.). Day_____

_____

2. When your family had a big event (a reunion, holidays, birthdays, weddings, funerals, etc.). Day____

_____

3. When socializing with high expectations (parties,

dances, dinners, bowling tournaments, club events, etc.). Day _____

_____

4. When taking a trip (business, vacation, shopping, across town, etc.). Day _____

_____

5. When entertaining (cleaning, decorating, hosting, making meals, sightseeing with visitors, etc.). Day

_____

_____

6. When there were changes in schedules and routines (at home to work, new roles, divorce, etc.). Day ___

_____

_____

7. When there were losses (plans fell through, loss of a relationship, death in the family, financial setbacks, job loss, etc.). Day_____

_____

8. When there were physical changes (pregnancy, illness, weight gain or loss, sexual problems, aging, etc.). Day _____

_____

9. When there were legal and money problems. Day

_____

_____

Now let's consider what you can do.

Preserving-Your-Perspective Checklist

1. Follow Your Patterns

Study your judgment. Make a chart or a list of the events that decrease your judging efficiency. How recent are these episodes? Do they occur more frequently than you realized?

2. Share Your List

Show that list or chart to someone you trust, perhaps someone you have begun talking to (see Chapter 17). See if that person has suggestions or additions.

3. Do You Defeat Yourself?

Write and discuss the ways in which you act against your own best interests. What is your usual style of coping? This material might be added to your daily journal (see Chapter 2).

4. Figure Out How To Counteract

Pick a plan to counteract the ways you have dealt with physical problems in the past. For example,

a. Get a daily calendar, either pocket size or refrigerator door compatible.

b. Put notes to yourself on the daily calendar about potential stressors during the day (a difficult meeting, road construction on the way to the meeting, little or no time for lunch, discussing your son's grades with his teacher, etc.).

c. Start to keep a small notebook, or collect "yellow stickies", perhaps at the end of the daily calendar. As they occur, write in episodes of daily threats to your judgments. This exercise will help you to get more tuned in to those events.

d. Figure out a reward that will help you stop when you catch yourself slipping into old behavior, e.g., an hour of something you enjoy, a movie, food, sex, a gift.

e. Give yourself a penalty if you catch yourself not being a good body "executive." Track the errors in your notebook, pay a fine to your piggybank, do a job that is difficult, do something for someone else that is difficult—at least that person will benefit!

f. Make an agreement with someone to help you stay alert to your own abuse. Don't punish them later for letting you know.

It is obvious that honesty is necessary for this process to work. It is difficult to look over our behavior and see some of our errors. Remember that the changes required probably will not be as great as you initially expected.

12. Laughing Out Loud

The most wasted day of all is that
on which we have not laughed.
Sebastian R. N. Chamfort

*For some, the energy required to control and monitor the
illness is so great that there is little time for anything else.
Without joy there is little reason or motivation to take on
the challenges of life or the struggle with an illness. The
chronic sufferer actively has to seek out experiences that
evoke a smile, a giggle or a hearty laugh.*

It has been said that perhaps the most distinguishing
feature separating human beings and lower animals is
the capacity to laugh. But that distinction becomes irrelevant if it is difficult to coax some humor out of a situation.
Depression and pain don't ordinarily lend themselves to
humorous repartee. But the combination can help you to
gain perspective, according to Rebecca Steinberg.

"I've never taken myself real seriously, but I certainly have taken trying to stay alive seriously," she says.

Humor often requires a suspension of belief, a removal of oneself from the predictable cause-and-effect
world in which we routinely expect certain things to
happen as the result of particular stimuli.

As in the Intensive Care Unit.

"You know, you're dealing with all that stuff plunged
into you," Sandra McCollum recounts, "and you're either
throwing up on yourself or you're incontinent. All these
just extraordinary sorts of things are happening and I
would always make some sort of a wise remark. I guess
that was a release, that if I could laugh about it, it didn't

have any power over me.

"The primary prerequisite for gripping onto my humanity and all the traits that make me unique is my sense of humor. A certain amount of craziness is a tremendous asset. For example, as I lie in a hospital bed with tubes and needles plugged into every available outlet in my body, I have found Lewis Carroll and Walt Disney to be two of my most entertaining mental companions. Somehow, the walrus, cabbages and kings, as well as all the lively and endearing creatures of the early Disney films, seem to put the insanity of the moment in the proper perspective.

"The primary recognition is that I have this illness; it does not have me. We inhabit the same body and we have jousted daily for so many years that we are old foes, but on speaking terms. Sometimes, when I'm very angry about not being able to breathe, I think of Peter Sellers as Inspector Clouseau screaming, 'Not now, Cato, you idiot!'

"These undisciplined lungs are something like that scenario—the illness may jump me and completely incapacitate me temporarily, but I'm still Sandra first, and only secondarily have this companion residing inside.

"Laughter is a wonderful anesthetic and an effective bronchodilator. I actively cultivate my sense of the ridiculous. In addition to numbing the pain and the occasional urge for self-pity, laughter makes my life interesting. And being involved and curious is a major way of living with a disease, instead of waiting to die with it.

"It's something to do to have power and control in your life. And I love to laugh. It's probably been the single most important thing to me after my faith, and I figure

God's got a good sense of humor. So that was sort of a gift that was given to me to help me to cope."

For the chronic sufferer, as for others, there are two contexts from which humor can be extracted: the present situation and a recollection, or memory, of a past humorous episode. Often, humor about yourself lets you step back for perspective or offers a breather from the upsets of a bad morning or a frustrating experience.

"If I am having a shaky day, I exercise humor," says Karen Stone. "It's not a matter of covering up, but a matter of being human. We all have shaky days. Laughter in this case is an amazing healer, very revealing and adds grace.

"Because I work on minimizing self-consciousness about my disability, I joke a lot about 'my speedy stride, my classy cane, my seemingly tipsy gait.' Co-workers pick up on this and continue the good-natured joking."

"Seek out people who make you feel good, whose company you enjoy, who make you laugh, who make you feel happy," Rebecca Steinberg advises. "Stay away from the people who bring you down."

Children often incorporate anger or meanness into their expressions of humor. Some psychologists suggest that, even as adults, humor is tinged with hostility or aggressive elements. We say someone has a biting humor, for example. One reason for finding humor in difficult, anguishing circumstances may be because somewhere in the back of our minds we know that humor might cover up anger. And dishing out anger, even disguised, can result in anger being returned.

It may seem odd that we are talking so much about

anger in a chapter that is supposed to be about humor. But by now, you have undoubtedly come to realize that one of the constant companions of your chronic illness is the feeling of frustration, of irritation with the limits put upon you by your disability. Anger is probably a familiar, almost comforting presence in its predictability.

One safe but useful way of using humor as a balm is to read something humorous or see a movie that may have made you laugh in the past. Perhaps videotapes of old TV reruns would be just the thing. In fact, reviewing old movies or TV shows serves two purposes: They help you recall a pleasant experience and they provide a releasing pleasure for the present. In particular, watching an old comedy with someone younger than yourself, someone who did not see it when it was first distributed can encourage a warmth and connection that may have been missing before.

Chapter Exercise

Jacquelin Goldman's Laughter File

This is an exercise to provide you with an emotional stash, an organized resource available to make you laugh on a rainy day, as it were. We learned of it from Dr. Jacquelin Goldman, a former psychology teacher of one of the authors.

Start by making a list of things that make you laugh. A minimum of 10 examples is a good start. Include movies, stories about yourself and your family, material from books and magazines, favorite jokes and cartoons (including the ones on the refrigerator door), pictures of people that force you to grin (pets can be included), humorous tapes or records (Cosby, Carlin, Martin, et al.), funny times with friends.

Don't expect the list to be exhaustive at first. In fact, look at it as an ever-expanding accumulation of humor and happiness as you add to it daily or weekly, or whenever you think something belongs there.

Set aside a place where your personal humor supply can be available and easily accessible. You might want to use index cards in the same way some people keep track of their recipes. Categorize the humor so that you can easily retrieve a particular joke or funny incident. For example, movie titles can be alphabetized and jokes can be arranged according to topic. Cartoons might have their own section. Or, to add to the enjoyment, you might want to leave things at random, so when you reach into your stash, you won't know exactly what will be making you laugh just then. Before you know it, you will have a whole file cabinet full of guffaws.

The pleasures of this exercise are fourfold.

1. Collecting the items. It's fun to pay attention to what makes you smile.

2. Pulling the material out when you are low and feeling the smile return like a warm sun emerging from behind the clouds.

3. Sharing pieces of your file with someone else—if you wish to.

4.   Knowing that no matter what your mood or circumstance is, regardless of the time of day or night, you have an immediate, sure-fire, already proven way to lift your spirits.

Theodora Abel's Bedside Humor

Theodora Abel is an esteemed therapist and wise woman whose more than nine decades of life continue to provide insight and awareness to friends and colleagues. This is her nightly routine. We can't promise you similar longevity, but we do think it's likely that you will be amused.

First, pay a leisurely visit to your local secondhand bookstore or drop in at your neighborhood library. Head for the humor section and select a manageable pile of softcover books written by humorists. At home, put them in a pile near your bed. Before turning off the light at night, and the last thing you do prior to going to sleep, read a few pages from any of the books. Do it often and pretty soon the habit will help you relax, while it gets you more familiar with the works of

    James Thurber
    Woody Allen
    Dave Barry
    Ogden Nash
    Erma Bombeck
    Sholem Aleichem

Bill Cosby
Mark Twain
Art Buchwald
P. G. Wodehouse

Start your own bibliography. It is illuminating to ask friends and family members older and younger than yourself to suggest names and titles. Subscribing to a magazine known for its humor can add substance and laughs to the bedside pile (*The New Yorker, Reader's Digest*). Check your library's magazine rack for additional possibilities.

13. Childhood Illnesses: Helping Your Child Cope

To travel hopefully is a better
thing than to arrive
Robert Louis Stevenson

Children face chronic illness with both depression and anger. They also have a unique flexibility and sense of energetic hope that older folks do not have. Chronic illnesses in children very sharply intrude upon their natural growth stages and influence the behavioral expectations of peers and authority figures. Caregivers need to be aware of how children's growth patterns will be affected by their chronic problems.

Psychologists have known for a long time that the play of children is the work of childhood. What we learn during our playtime—the existence of rules, the importance of getting along with others, the joy of accomplishment, the ability to rebound from failure, the self-sustaining vigor of alone time—serves us well as adults.

"I remember feeling bad that I couldn't run out to play with the other kids," Sandra McCollum remembers about her childhood. "But I loved books and I loved school and I could be best at that."

Role playing is one important way younger children start to define who they are and thereby gain a sense of how they will be treated or responded to. All of us have watched a child as she acts out her conception of a police officer, astronaut, mother, father, and other adult figures.

As they grow older, children begin to be better able to select traits and qualities of others which they see as desirable. Models of who and what they would specifically like to become are a focus of their interest. Sandra McCollum's childhood interest in Wilma Rudolph is one such example. We sometimes call that hero worship. It is, among other things, a powerful ingredient of many television and magazine advertisements.

As a result, children with chronic illnesses look to adults for guidance, for cues as to how to handle this intrusion into their lives which their friends have escaped. Like a child from a divorced family, the boy or girl with a chronic illness may direct anger toward the parent with whom she associates the daily routine of coping with the frustrating circumstances in which she finds herself. The child might even blame the parent for the pain and distress. In turn, parents may feel helpless, self-blaming, and angry themselves.

Informal results from a questionnaire administered to youngsters attending an overnight asthma camp provide some evidence for this. Asked to complete the sentence fragment. "A mother...," a surprising number offered uncomplimentary responses:

A mother

. . . makes you take medicine.

. . . is a pain.

. . . is too protective.

. . . is an asshole.

. . . is a pain in the ass.

. . . is a pest.

Assuredly, most questionnaires contained favorable or neutral sentence completions about mothers. But two things are striking. One, fathers received virtually no negative responses, and it was the mothers who participated most in the treatment of their children—which helps to explain why they were the parent at whom much emotion was directed.

Some of the positive answers reflected this:

A mother

. . . is someone who is always there when needed.

. . . is someone who cares.

. . . is loving and caring and helps their [sic] child do her fullest with whatever they want to do in life.

One explanation for the different responses may be related to distortion on the mother's part. Studies indicate that it is perhaps not the actual severity of an illness that is critical, but instead whether the mother's perception is skewed or accurate. Research psychiatrists have found that in instances in which mother either overestimates or underestimates the extent of the illness, the child is "more likely" to be overprotected. Family life is also affected.

Thus, it is possible that children with negative attitudes toward parents, especially the main caretaker, mother, are at times expressing dissatisfaction with the mother's perception of the illness.

Furthermore, because children, particularly adolescents, often see their parents as being unduly restrictive, overprotective mothers are viewed as being even more limiting than usual. This is especially true of mothers who overestimate the severity of the child's illness.

On a more positive note, mothers may be blamed because they are seen as strong enough to absorb their children's suffering and anger.

To compound matters, and as pointed out in the Introduction, adults often understand and respond to illness and misfortunes based on their own childhood experiences. So the mixture of past and present perceptions can have a confusing and distorting effect on the parent-child relationshi. However, the formula and the outcome of that equation can sometimes be reversed.

"My mother had chronic illness trouble and this was inherited," Sandra McCollum recounts. "And it sounds kind of funny to say it, but that was my biggest blessing because my father was terrified, just terrified, when I wanted to do things, like go to school or work or be involved in activities. It hurt him to see me suffer. Mother understood and so she would encourage me. She would say 'Go ahead.' It's impossible to calculate the value of that extraordinary support."

Children with a chronic illness already have conflicting and changing feelings of sadness, depression, and anger. While the sadness may be turned inward, the anger can be expressed outwardly. Questions about who is to blame and why things can't be fixed are salient to these children. After all, particularly for younger children, if parents are seen as all-knowing and all-fixing creatures in other areas of daily family life (Daddy and Mommy, for example, can take care of a bruised knee or a broken bicycle), then why aren't they able to get rid of my activity-restricting asthma or food-intake-restricting diabetes? For young children, that is a perplexing conundrum—and an anger-producing one as well.

Sandra McCollum views it, from her own experience, in an attitudinal and communication context.

"Now we call them positive affirmations," Sandra McCollum notes. "But when I was a kid there was always this inherent thing to focus on: What I could do and never to say never. Whether it was the Little Engine That Could, if you have setbacks, don't say you can't do it because you failed once. Language is very important."

And so is the message that language communicates.

"We refuse to look at it in a negative light," Elizabeth Strong says of daughter Jeanne's diabetes. "It may have a physical hold on her, but we're trying not to let it have an emotional hold. Put your mind in the positive and take it one day at a time."

It seems to be working for the 12-year-old gymnast. Her friends, Jeanne says wistfully, "get to eat candy and stuff that I can't have." Her parents, though, "help me take care of my diabetes. I guess it works out okay." But she admits being angry at her sister when she gets sweets that are forbidden to Jeanne.

Jeanne's parents have made an effort to control the younger child's consumption of candy. "But we've not restricted her completely," Elizabeth says, implicitly acknowledging the fine line the family has to tread.

One of the more sustained, unlearned exertions of infants is the strenuous, sometimes almost violent, response to physical restraint. When movement is restricted, babies only a few weeks or months old will bellow at the tops of their lungs, struggle furiously, and show other signs of what can properly be labeled angry behavior. How that anger is alleviated—by calm, quick removal of the inhibiting factors, for example, or impersonal, noncomforting delayed attention, or distraction with a warm bottle of milk—has a profound effect on the child's later reactions to frustrating and restricting experiences.

Thus, the 5-year-old who is told he must not exert himself because of lung deficiency is likely to build up a well of resentment. Or the 13-year-old with diabetes, told she cannot eat the same kinds of foods as do her peers, may verbally strike out at the restricter of her diet. In short, we are tapping a primitive and early experience that has its foundations at the beginning of life.

Similarly, sadness and anger become intertwined as the child grieves the loss of prowess and the expected diminishing of future opportunities and abilities.

"Asthma is a pain in the butt," one 14-year-old boy proclaims. "I can't run. Sports suck. When I was younger, I was athletic."

Another says, "Compared to most kids I have to worry about my asthma and it makes me more responsible."

"Sports," says a 16-year-old girl with asthma, "are okay if you can breathe after playing them!"

Jay Sellers, an active 17-year-old diagnosed with cystic fibrosis two weeks after birth, speaks enthusiastically about the close, supportive relationship he has with his mother and father.

"I'm really close to my parents," he says, "and I think it has to do with CF because I guess they kinda give me the extra added attention. They've been right beside me every step of the way."

Building on the strength gained from his family, which includes an older sister who also has cystic fibrosis, Jay says that despite the illness, "you can't wallow in self-pity. If you do that, your life is going to be destroyed. Accept it as a challenge, not your ultimate nemesis."

He adds, "Sometimes you have to grieve, I guess. Like sometimes when you hear about someone with CF dying. You kinda have to think about it. You can't just blow it off. A little self-pity comes in then. You just have to acknowledge your limits, your own mortality.

"I don't begrudge anyone their health. It would be nice to be like them, but you're not and that's just the way it is."

The task, then, of childhood remains play; but for the chronically ill its purpose is altered by the presence of premature responsibility, early loss of predictability, and battles with emotions that ordinarily are not confronted so dramatically until the self has become more secure and comfortable.

The task, then, of the parent is to acknowledge the emotional dynamics of the child while assessing the accuracy of the perceived severity of the illness. Consulting with the child's professional caretaker is, of course, critical here. But our old friend, denial, must also be included in any such discussion, and considered when calculating the always-fluctuating equation.

Diane Sorenson, 13, enjoys the feel of foot speed and amateur competition. She also knows she has exercise-induced asthma.

"I wanted to be on the track team since I was little," she says matter-of-factly. "I even beat the boys when I was in the first grade."

In the seventh grade, Diane, who already had done well at volleyball, went out for the track team.

"I really like to run," she says. "I do it until I have trouble breathing."

Diane participated for a week or so, using an inhaler both before and after she ran. Her mother, Joyce, remembers her daughter returning home with terrible headaches and shaking. "So I said no. We had talked about it, are the consequences worth it? After a while, she didn't think so either."

"The determination from Diane was there to keep doing this every day, coming home exhausted and shaking, saying she didn't feel like eating.

"Diane kept saying, 'I want to do this. I want to do this.' She was angry but became resigned to the fact that she couldn't do it. She was exercising extreme denial: 'This will be better tomorrow.'"

Upset and frustrated, but not entirely surprised, Diane heard her mother suggest that she remain involved with the team, perhaps as manager.

"I thought that was stupid," Diane says, "because in track, there's only running." But the desire to keep her connection with the sport and her friends was strong.

As team manager, Diane recorded times and took attendance. Most important, she was able to bridge the change from active participant-competitor to active participant-helper. At one point during the season, the team needed a fourth runner to allow it to compete in an important relay race. On the bus ride to the meet, some team members and coaches put pressure on Diane. The experience made her angry.

"I really wanted to compete, but I didn't. I told them I wouldn't be able to do it and I didn't have the right shoes."

"She was pretty upset by the track episode," Diane's mother remembers.

When basketball season came around, Diane was there running suicide drills. After some rigorous preseason exposure to these court-length capacity-building exercises, Diane developed a persistent cough and other symptoms. Her mother was about to tell her to quit the team when Diane herself put an end to it because, she said, she was unhappy with the coach.

"She was trying so hard in basketball. She tried so hard, I think some of her anger became directed toward the coach." Joyce adds, "I want her to do as much as she can, but I wouldn't let it get to the danger point. I don't want any more trips to the emergency room. It's frightening when you see your kid having serious trouble breathing."

"When I first found out I had asthma, I was really, really mad," Diane says, recalling the restrictions the new diagnosis placed upon her. "I pouted."

"And whined," her mother interjects. Now Diane says, "I laugh at myself when I hurt myself, I laugh with my friends about it. It's mainly all you can do."

Not quite.

Determined, Diane plans to try again to be a member of the track team—but not as manager. With the advice and help of her doctor, and the support of her mother, Diane is carefully preparing to participate in short-distance competition. As part of the aggressive effort to try to effectively control the problem, she has learned how to use a breath monitor to check her lung capacity. It's all become just part of the routine.

As a result, Diane's belief is firm when she says, "I don't really think of asthma as a disease. I think of diabetes or epilepsy as a disease, but not asthma."

Her mother concurs with that perception. "Diane," she says, "thinks of it more as a condition of life. We've communicated about the management of this condition with her doctor and maybe that's why she doesn't think of it as a disease.

"I'm convinced that one reason she has as few problems as she does, is that Diane realizes she has control. It's her condition. I can't be with her every minute, and I felt it was important that she understand what was going on. She's the one who has to maintain her ability to breathe through her medications.

"No one can look over her to see she takes her inhaler on time. It's been a lesson in communication, and I think she does have a real good sense of it. I think she has a real good attitude about it, most of the time. I make Diane feel responsible for what she can do and can't do."

Diane smiles as her mother speaks. Self-confident, looking toward the future, she seems like an adolescent without any adult-imposed cares in the world. Only a year or so earlier, Diane had finished a 400-meter race when she suddenly couldn't breathe. The problem was so severe she was unable even to communicate her distress to a nearby teacher. Quickly, a friend read the symptoms and rushed Diane to the school nurse. Diane clearly remembers the terrible fear—and something else.

"I still came in third, though," she says with a smile of self-confidence.

Chapter Exercise

The task here is to help parent(s) and child relate to each other's understanding of the chronic illness and to correct misunderstandings patiently and with respect for what everyone is going through. Sometimes it is easier to communicate indirectly.

The Consensual Sentence Completion

The Consensual Sentence Completion should be filled out separately by each member of the family *from the point of view of the child with the chronic illness*. That is, respond to it as if you were the person with the disability. (Of course, the chronic illness sufferer is to fill it out, also.) You can make blank copies for all family members. It is best to fill out the entire form separately at one sitting.

1. Things at home that make me feel better are _____
    _____

2. The best activity we do at home is _____
    _____

3. I have most fun alone when I'm doing_____
    _____

4. When I go to the doctor, I'd rather go with _____
    _____

5. When my friends call, I like it if my parents_____
    _____

6. My favorite TV show is_____
    _____

7. I like it because_____
    _____

8. It bugs me when my mother _____

9. It bugs me when my father_____

10. I get angriest when_____

11. Taking my medicine makes me feel_____

12. In school, the other kids think I_____

13. It bugs me when my brother/sister_____

14. The worst thing about my illness is_____

15. My illness interferes a lot, a little, in between with the things I like to do. (Circle one.)

After everyone has completed all the sentences, it is suggested that a quiet time acceptable to everyone be chosen. Set aside about 30 minutes when no interruptions are expected. Compare answers by having all members read aloud their responses. This is not a gripe or criticism session. It is a time to see how miscommunication and misunderstandings can be remedied. The goal is to try to adjust behavior when perceptions or feelings don't match.

If agreement can't be worked out at this session, arrange to meet again in two weeks to go over remaining areas of difficulty. If friction remains and interferes with routine family functioning, consider counseling.

Filling out the Consensual Sentence Completion periodically can be useful for ongoing communication between the chronically ill child and other members of the family. It helps to compare perspective.

It's not a
final distance
this here
and now.
Robert Creeley

*A new diagnosis of chronic illness can have a range of
emotional impact. The past becomes distorted and the
future seems uncertain. The present is confused. It is
important at this time to be calm and patient and to learn
what to expect so you can be prepared for what is to come.*

Don't run away. This chapter may be helpful to you.

Most people who have just been diagnosed would not
be ready to open a book such as this one. That you have
already done so puts you a step or two ahead. This section
explains why. Perhaps it will make the process of moving
on more understandable and less frustrating.

Most likely, your diagnosis did not come suddenly or
unexpectedly. Medical tests, doctor consultations, informal information from friends and relatives, your own self-
monitoring of your body—a variety of sources prepared
you, at least at some level, for the possibility of a major
change in your life. Still, the news was a shocking blow,
and adjustments had to be made.

As Karen Stone put it after multiple sclerosis put an
end to a full plate of vigorous pursuits in the outdoors,
"You can't climb mountains, but you can climb mountains
of a different sort."

It is important to know at the outset that many
people will, through trial-and-error efforts, ultimately

settle on their own style of coping with the demands of their illness. A wide range of individual response styles is chronicled throughout this book. Of course, there is no way to predict how one person will respond to complex medical news.

There are, however, patterns of emotional behavior that are regularly found in the majority of individuals who have recently lost an important part of who they are—mobility, a limb, self-esteem, a dream. Your chronic illness, regardless of its severity, prognosis or type, involves loss. And we now have enough accumulated research evidence to enable us to outline the emotional stages likely to be encountered from loss experienced by the newly diagnosed chronic illness sufferer.

Elisabeth Kubler-Ross, a psychiatrist, wrote about reactions to loss in *On Death and Dying*. Her landmark work,published in 1969, was the first to describe in detail a person's reactions to the permanent loss of a family member or friend. But the process she observed in one arena of human existence—mortality—has come to include an understanding of the human response to *any* loss—missing a bus about to pull away; loss of a close relationship such as a lover or friend; disappointment over a promotion not awarded; diminished physical capacity; a misplaced or stolen wallet or purse.

Being told you have a disabling disease can, of course, be life-changing. The loss is a blow to who you are, who you have been, and who you will become. The emotional aftershocks can be pervasive and persistent. But they do not have to be life-long.

It does not matter if the loss of functioning is large

or small. It does not matter if treatment will help to some degree or not. In fact, later on these factors may become irrelevant. But at first, just the words "chronic" and "permanent" make you feel extreme stress.

"Give yourself some time," Peter Clifton advises. "You may need to wait a couple of years to find what you can do and where you're at before you make any sort of decisions on the ultimate disposal of your life. By that time, you may decide that, well, hell, it's a drag to sit down and have to run around in a wheelchair, but it's still a lot of fun and there are things to do, and let's see how it works out, let's see how this play ends."

Pat Pathkiller weighed 259 pounds and had a blood glucose level rocketing skyward when, at age 45, she found out she had diabetes. The doctor told Pat, a Native American from Oklahoma, that she would have to remain bedridden if she expected the ulcers on her legs to heal. She shook her head, eyes filling with tears. She moved to pick up her things and leave the doctor's office.

"And he came up to me—here's this tall white man, and I'm a pretty tall Indian woman—and he took me by the shoulders and looked right into my face and said, 'Don't you want to live?' Well, I decided I did want to live. And that really turned my life around."

Since chronic illness involves loss, Kubler-Ross's stages of reactions, which are overlapping and more or less sequential, apply similarly to how you feel when the diagnosis is made. There are five sets of reactions, all probably more or less personally familiar to those who have grieved the loss of a departed friend or family member. Look at them carefully, and perhaps you will see yourself in one or all of the phases.

1. **Denial** ("It can't be! Not to me! I'm as healthy as I've ever been.")

2. **Anger** ("I hate this and anyone who is not sick is getting off easy!")

3. **Depression** ("All is lost and nothing matters any more.")

4. **Bargaining** ("I'll be good. I'll change. Just give me one more chance.")

5. **Acceptance** ("I now realize that this is my circumstance, my condition. Even though I do not deserve it, I have to make the best of it.")

As you might imagine, the stages do not follow one another in precise order. On the contrary, they appear and reappear in unpredictable fashion, slowly moving toward longer periods of acceptance. It is in the acceptance phase that the real work of long-term adaptation to a disability begins.

Let's look at each stage one by one.

Denial

The doctor has just told you that your aches and pains, recently intensified and disturbing, are due to arthritis. There is no cure, but there are medications that will ease the discomfort. The prognosis is not clear; tests are still being run. However, for the time being, the doctor asks you to do only mild to moderate exercise. This is a far cry from the softball and bicycle riding that have filled your evenings and weekends for years.

The reaction of denial might sound like this:

1. The diagnosis is a mistake; it can't be.

2. The doctor is not too familiar with arthritis, anyway.

3. The diagnosis is not complete—it's probably wrong.

4. My body is fine; I'll do what I want.

5. I'm going bike riding as planned on Sunday.

6. I've never felt better.

7. I'll wake up soon—it's a bad dream.

Denial is hard to maintain for long periods, as reality ultimately comes crashing down. But sometimes it provides a brief respite. It also confuses people who care about you and who know the truth.

When Carol Wiseman learned that her daughter, Jessica, 12, had diabetes, she found coping with the new demands of the situation to be "trauma city." But she plugged on.

"Once you're educated, it clears out the fears of the

unknown. If you don't educate yourself, you're asking for disaster to happen. Everyone has some denial at first. But you reach a point where you have to say, 'This is not going to go away. I am going to have to deal with it.'"

She recommends joining an organization like a local chapter of the American Diabetes Association. "Go to those classes," she advises. "They'll help you understand the worries and denial that you have."

For Andy Nordstrum, the denial issues were perhaps more difficult to sort out. Nordstrum, a clinical psychologist, went to the doctor after passing out after ignoring "this funny feeling in my chest" while working out on his rowing machine. The doctor told him it sounded like a heart problem.

"I was surprised," Andy remembers. "The EKG was abnormal. I was convinced it was normal. I'm smoking a pack a day, thinking heart discomfort was coming from my lungs. I thought maybe it was lung cancer or emphysema.

"I did a treadmill. It was abnormal, too. I think: 'The next test, it will be corrected.' I had an angiogram. The doctor says, 'There are two blockages. The pain is angina.'" The doctor, medically conservative, recommends angioplasty. "It's your choice," he tells Andy. Andy demurs.

"I try to get a sense of how serious it is. 'You are saying that if I keep up this stuff, smoking, not eating right, no exercising, then in a couple of years, I will have a heart attack?' 'No,' the doctor says, 'in a couple of days.'

"I am furious, I scream. I want to buy a pack of cigarettes. I was sure I was getting off this train. I was livid. I'll be damned—giving up smoking. I like to play sports. I don't like to exercise. It was August. I didn't quit smoking until February."

Clearly, denial and anger are intimately connected in the grieving process.

Anger

Anger and fury are another part of the reaction to loss. People feel abused and persecuted by their illness. They are angry about their bodies, their doctors, their illness. They let others know. While this response is normal and appropriate, those around may feel hurt and injured by the anger that is projected like blasts of grit-filled wind.

Those who observe the person struggling wonder why they seem to be the target of the anger. ("I didn't do anything. I'm only trying to help.") But the anger is profound, it is deeply real. As such, it needs time to dissipate.

It is the kind of anger that we read about in the Bible or Greek mythology as heroes go through suffering. After centuries have passed, we remain transfixed by the stories like those of Job and Ulysses in which we discover that as human beings we are truly vulnerable to unfair and unpredictable fate. The resonance with our own vulnerability, our own mortality, rings intimately true.

Thus, we might hear the person with the arthritis diagnosis (or other chronic illness) saying things like

1. Why me? I work hard. I don't bother anyone.
2. Why not you? Look at *your* flaws.

3. This is not fair. It pisses me off.
4. I hate life. I've been betrayed.
5. I hate my body—it's useless.
6. I hate healthy people—showoffs!
    They're getting off easy.
7. I hate watching people having fun.
8. I hate my feelings of hate.

Anger is intense. But it too passes.

"In my darkest moments," Ken Saville, born with polio, admits, "when suddenly I have a lot of pain in the last 24 hours—and I haven't strained myself, I didn't overtax myself, I haven't done anything to make it hurt, I'm doing good stuff—I think to myself, 'Why does this happen to me? Why can't the pain be spread out? There are bad people in the world. Why can't they have the pain?'"

Beth Salazar, 45, found that her ire was a double-edged sword. "My anger helped me get rid of sadness and helplessness," she remembers about her post-accident arthritis. "But keeping the anger too long can turn it into a negative force. It can become a poison in one's life."

Depression and Despair

Depressed and despairing, the person feels catastrophically wounded and unable to see any light at the end of the proverbial tunnel. Friends, family members, and fellow workers notice that the object of their concern seems quiet, withdrawn, irritable.

Activities are not enjoyed and weight gain or loss

may suddenly occur. Sleeping—either too much or too little—is a problem, and agitation or immobility may appear. Depressed people are tired and feel both worthless and self-critical. They cannot concentrate and are indecisive. They may even express suicidal thinking.

Our newly diagnosed chronic illness person may feel

1. It's all over. All is lost.
2. I can't do anything anymore.
   I won't see my family again.
3. Nobody cares.
4. I'd rather be dead than alive.
5. Nothing is fun anymore.
6. I am useless.
7. My life is one mistake after another.
8. Leave me alone.

This phase is important. Often it passes, but if it does not, you must seek professional help. Clearly, the depressed stage can seriously interfere with what is necessary to get better.

Psychiatrist Neil Bischkoff, 57, more than 20 years later, remembers his reaction to being told in 1971 about what the doctors considered to be a serious, but undefined, EKG abnormality.

"I thought I'd die. What it did was, emotionally I went through mourning. It was as though I died. I felt like a walking dead man on death row. I felt like crying. I was brooding, morose, planning for afterwards to get things up-to-date, to say goodbye.

"I looked at the kids like it was the last time. I purged myself of attachment. I started my clinical practice with ambivalence. I began to live my life as if every day was the last day. I made all decisions on what was important to me as if it were my last day."

Rebecca Steinberg provides a good example of the overlapping quality of the stages—in this case, depression and acceptance. "It's okay to be depressed," she says, "if there's a reason to be depressed."

Bargaining

During the bargaining stage the person quietly and silently hopes for one more chance. Here we have the negotiator and wheeler-dealer that exists in everyone.

The dialogue goes on between the person and fate, God, medicine, and one's own conscience.

1. I'll stop yelling at my spouse, just make me better.
2. I won't drink again, please give me back my old body.
3. I will go to church twice a week, and I know I will improve.
4. I will call my mother more often, just give me another chance.
5. I will try to be kinder if you give me a break.

"Sometimes, when I'm sick, I start to figure out all the things I did wrong in the last week," one of our patients told us. "I promise myself I will eat okay, take it easy, go to sleep on time . . . for a few days. Maybe the bad feeling will go away. Usually by the time I'm under the weather, it's too late. But the whole process feels like it might work—you know, if I say I'll be good."

Bargaining is not strange or bizarre. It is a normal reaction to the perception that the illness is a punishment. The person feels like a child asking a parent for one more chance to be good. It would not hurt any of us to be nicer to our family, to limit our drinking, to call home, and attend to our spiritual needs more often. But, as we know, that seldom erases illness.

Acceptance

The last stage of mourning a loss, acceptance implies a coming to terms with your own situation. It doesn't mean accepting your status in terms of giving in to it; nor does it imply complete control over all facets of its symptomatology. What it does mean is that an emotional understanding has emerged wherein you recognize that the loss has made you different-while-still-the-same and that your new status will require new skills and concentrated work.

You may hear yourself saying

1. I have an illness, but I still am okay.
2. This pain will not stop me from growing.
3. I will try many new things to improve my life in this new phase.
4. I have much to learn and do.
5. There are options that I do not know about. I would like to seek them out.
6. This is my circumstance. I will make the best of it.

Mary Alice Kerr has lived with her multiple sclerosis for more than a year and knows the possibility remains that further deterioration may yet occur.

"If that happens, then I want to know what I'm going to do . . . which will be to go to the Denver School for the Blind. I want to know what my options are. I have to keep the future open in both directions.

"I also enjoy what I have now, the capacities I can use today, because I don't know what the future holds. You need to figure out how to restructure your life so that the things you're doing now are important and how that can mean something in terms of your growth." Just have something going on, so you will have something to hold on to. There are times that can seem really empty, so trying to find out how it's not really empty is important."

Allan Pike is both more specific and more general. "Why limit myself?" he muses about his thinking after he got married. "Why live in fear of what *might* happen? I took each day as it came, not worrying about the future. I had always enjoyed the beauty of life. It just became more acute."

Each stage reflects your conscious and unconscious attempts to make meaning out of that which is unreasonable and unfair. We do not want to be sick or disabled. We do not wish to lose body functions. We did not invite illness. It is all an intrusion into our psychological space. The newness of it presents a blending of anguish and surprises, not all of them unpleasant.

"Fate and faith is an interesting dance, so I've discovered recently," Karen Stone wrote in a letter just prior to returning to work not long after her diagnosis of multiple sclerosis was confirmed. "I guess they follow each other in that order.

"Having been so slowed down these past few months has been like riding a river raft: I'm over stiller waters now, but deeper, too. I have had a chance to dive off, to deep crawl, to sense both the depth and the strength of the current.

"Riding ripples, as I did a lot of in the past, is too fast, and, of course, too shallow. Swimming the deeper waters takes a bit of courage, strength, and oxygen. With the lack of coordination that has occurred, there has been the added grace of understanding and love. I thought I had that already, but as a friend once said, 'Nobody can predict a surprise!'

"I have seen something new—how kind people really are. Walking with a cane, slowly, causes people to rush to the door and hold it open for me. And they look into my eyes, too. And smile.

"Now, this is very new. I've usually done this for others. The effect is that of a softening, not self-pity, of added renewal and faith in people, including myself. So the fate of getting slowed down to see this has certainly been the positive side."

"There is no end to the rainbow," Susan Abeyta concludes. "I could improve the odds, but that was all. At some point, I had to let go—whatever happens, happens."

So, if the doctor just told you that you have a physical problem that will not heal, do not be surprised if your initial reaction is numbness or fury or depression or even mental "deals" with fate. These are all signs of being human and therefore being vulnerable to our unreliable bodies and our mortal state.

You are entering a change that seems sudden but is really a slow metamorphosis. Your body is evolving and so is your mind. Yesterday you felt invulnerable. Today you know you are not. Tomorrow you may find new and surprising strengths. You are part of an ever-increasing group of people your age and older who are discovering that their once-perfect, or at least more or less predict-able, body is no longer so perfect or predictable.

Still, you may be assuming that life before the diagnosis is gone, a thing of the past. The hours you spent playing racquetball, dancing, hiking, traveling, enjoying your hobby, enjoying your children and grandchildren are now only memories. More likely than not, this isn't true. You are making a serious mistake if you prematurely grieve for your life before having seen a doctor recently.

We live in a time that presents many options, both medically and personally. There are ways to connect the past, the present, and the future. Karen Stone, a climber of mountains and forger of rivers prior to her illness, calls them bridges—connections or linkages between the (no longer available) pleasures and joys of your former self and the related activities and joys of who you are now. Building a bridge, of course, takes time and requires its own special kind of endurance.

"I'm not gifted with super powers," Karen says. "As a matter of fact, I went through all the stages a person encounters after a loss, like denial, anger, and grief. In the process, though, I finally began to understand how pa-tience works. In fact, when you walk as slowly as I do, you become practiced in patience. Simply, things cannot move any faster for me.

"Patience is my spiritual glue. During the first few months of my physical disability, while I was dealing with emotional upheavals, two things helped tremendously: the loving support of those around me, including the understanding of the vice president of my firm, and being able to spend solitary time outdoors, in my garden.

"The vice president gave me a leave of absence of my choosing. He also said, 'Name your hours when you return.' The garden gave the space to yell and scream at the greater cosmos, while at the same time nature's gentleness made my tears feel less anguished."

Karen's job as marketing coordinator for a large architectural/engineering company served as its own bridge during the early stages of her newly diagnosed illness.

"Continuing to work became my anchor. While the emotional side has been a roller coaster, work has been a regular heartbeat throughout, offering the steady rhythm so necessary during such changing times. It's another drop of steadfast glue."

Bridges abound. Nature provides for the mountain climber and hiker as well as the gardener and park stroller. "Like all mortals, I feel the vulnerability walking right alongside me," Karen acknowledges. "I get scared or overwhelmed or simply tired.

"I also am aware that at such moments, I have to do one of two things immediately: Be with another human being or go into the garden—preferably both. As soon as I am with someone else, the focus is on that person. I feel their aches, their sharingness, their goodness, whatever.

"And, of course, the garden is a place that consistently reeks of resurgence, of life, of response to my efforts. A nice rescue, always."

There are other bridges for other people.

When Jim "Catfish" Hunter, the Oakland Athletics and New York Yankees Hall of Fame pitcher, suddenly learned at age 31 that he had diabetes during spring training in 1977, he was sure his life was over. The Yankee team doctor remembers the righthander's condition as being "pretty severe . . . . If we had not detected it then, he would have gone into a diabetic coma within a few days."

"I thought that was it," Hunter, who retired in 1979, recalls. "I was going to die. I wouldn't play anymore. I wouldn't see my kids much longer."

But within a month, his attitude took a dramatic turn. The only difference in his lifestyle, he discovered, involves watching his blood sugar levels and making sure he eats the right food.

"I wanted to talk to everybody about it," he says, "tell them I'm a diabetic, so they'd know about it. I never wanted to keep it a secret. It was important for others to know they could get on with their lives. I told people about it as a practical matter."

Peter Clifton was athletic and physically active prior to an incomplete paraplegia, the result of a motorcycle accident at age 31. He used to ski; he still skis. The bridge for him was not a change of activity, but a modification of how he participated in the activity.

"You need a little extra equipment," he says quietly. But his sense of accomplishment is palpable.

"When I finally figured out how to do it, and I made my first high speed run down Porcupine Hill in Taos, that was really a revelation because that is something you can do just as good as people who stand up—even better.

"It's such a thrill. I get a real kick out of it. Going up the lift, you see people coming down on monoskis, people on sitskis, blind people, people with one leg, and there were stand-up skiers and snowboarders.

"So you look and see all these people sliding down the mountain. You say, 'Look at this. This is pretty cool.' That was as close as I came to having a real revelation as to what can be done.

"Now I like winter better than summer."

As someone who found sports to be a source of confidence, Andy Nordstrum had to make a similar adjustment. At age 19, nerves in his hand were functionally dead from ALS.

"It's hard to open doors," he recalls of the time. "It's not terribly manly. I have to grab them with two hands. Rough, if you're out with a girl. My tendency was to tell people about it.

"I still play softball—second base [with its shorter throwing distance to first], not third. I could not hold on to the bat. I learned to play tennis two-handed. I looked good before and now I look goofy."

Or perhaps you were attracted to the joys of food and your doctor has told you—a first for you—that your diet must drastically change. "The largest thorn in my side is food and changing food habits," Pat Pathkiller acknowledges.

But the bridge from forbidden foods to edible eats need not be narrow or long. Others already have explored the way. Pat attends a diabetes group as often as she can.

"We need all the support we can get," she says, "because we have to learn to handle food. I always come away feeling better, with new recipes. You know you're not alone."

Bridges may be active or passive. They may serve to

telescope an activity enjoyed in the past into a more manageable size. The inveterate moviegoer, for example, knows this only too well when she gets tired earlier and watches a video at home at 7 P.M. instead of getting to the theater for a 9:15 showing. Or the circumstances of a former activity may be applicable to the present.

Helen Baer, 41, was a track athlete in high school.

"When you race, you organize the rest of your life to do that. Medical treatment for diabetes and cancer was a physical challenge. If I concentrated on the physical challenge, I could get through well. It was familiar and it made it seem less frightening. There would be a lifetime to integrate the rest. It didn't need to be a crisis. It could be a point of focus."

There are also ways to link hospital stays with life temporarily left behind.

"I had this sort of antique little blue Samsonite tote and I had it packed with my own gowns and some books," Sandra McCollum explains. "At the last minute before leaving for the hospital, I would throw in things like my Walkman, the one I use when I ride my bike.

"So when I see it in the hospital, then there's this connection back to life, a connection back to the things that I did in health. Somebody once asked me if it didn't depress me to see a picture by my hospital bed of my husband and me standing on the beach. That was for me sort of an incentive to move, that if I could look like that and I could do that, then I could survive.

"So I had my own shampoo, my own comb, my watch. All these things were attempts to have some control in a setting where there was little or no control."

There is one final area to consider as you digest and make part of yourself the new facts, new feelings, and new frustrations associated with your changed status. Consider your own thoughts, memories, and associations around illness. Sometimes, these are tainted so that you will feel more helpless than necessary.

If you have had childhood experiences where your body has failed you, they will affect how you feel now. If you watched a brother, sister, mother, or father struggle to overcome significant or long-term medical obstacles, you are likely to use that as a guide to what will happen to you.

If you have watched a family member or childhood friend become disabled when you were little, you may have memories of the expectations and approaches to illness that are outdated. Perhaps your memories are laden with the feeling that when someone is chronically ill, it meant that person was "through," forgotten, unable to function, and to be pitied.

Maybe there are others in your life who, because *your* new diagnosis has brought a change in their relationship to you, unexpectedly have resurrected their own earlier memories of illness and disease. They, too, may experience a distancing from you that can be bridged only by communication and understanding. Not only are you not familiar with your new role and self-concept, those around you are not sure, either. The resulting dance of uncertainty, feeling out the limits and appropriate response patterns of the new relationship, is a significant aspect of your new diagnostic status.

"Because my co-workers and I struggled through

watching the changes that occurred in me over a two-year period, we had some time to talk, digest, and assimilate the nature of disability," Karen Stone writes. "Fortunately, the nondisabled people had similar needs to understand, to help, and to grow. Because of this, the efforts at communication worked.

"In the process, our vulnerabilities surfaced. Like death, our fears are a taboo subject in this society. So initially I needed to reach deep within and share instead a sense of strength to diminish the scariness, so we could face the realities and carry on with our work.

"Strength, always and in all ways an admirable quality in people, is not really a matter of discussion, but rather a sensed and felt quality. Likewise, strength cannot be purchased. It is developed slowly through a myriad of methods: religious practice; meditation; faith; work with professional help—you name it—and developed experientially.

"We cannot rush strength. It has its own terms."

Chapter Exercise

Track Feelings

As always, it is your job to think about how you would like things to go. You will be able to control more than you expect. Your mind can help you make the best of this new state of affairs. Remember that your mind stays ready to learn and adapt. You may find that this will be an important experience that will lead you to enjoy and learn about new things, perhaps acquire new skills and become more aware of your common humanity.

Talking to someone close to you is always a good way to explore your feelings. Among other things, you are likely to discover that others have suffered too and have overcome obstacles. Get information from established health organizations, particularly those associated with your particular illness. Always remember: Whatever you are experiencing has been experienced by someone else. You can learn from that.

When you get past denial, you may be able to write down some of your thoughts and feelings. Start by getting a notebook. A simple one will do. It is not necessary to spend time thinking about what you will write. Now, with the notebook in front of you, and seated in a comfortable, quiet spot with no expectation of interruption, put down your thoughts in a letter to yourself, to your healthier self from yesterday, to your doctor, to God, to your favorite person, or to an imaginary person. You might wish to use Kubler-Ross's stages as an outline for your letter. Write knowing there is no expectation of actually showing the letter, unless you feel you want to.

If this is too "personal," or uncomfortable for you, perhaps a journal format will be easier. (See Chapter 2 for a more detailed description of journal writing.) You will be surprised to see your words. Write them when you are alone. Most people like to have a set, daily time and place to write in their journal. Put the notebook away and write in it regularly. Write your reactions as possible responses to the statement, "Thinking about my illness, I feel . . ."

In our culture, it is not typical to write down our reactions to experience. But, if we look at history, theology, psychology, literature, and medicine, we find a long tradition of writing and tracking events and feelings. All these disciplines recognized the importance of writing down what we experience. This age-old method can help you sort through your feelings about your new diagnosis.

Remember that when denial ends (it always does, eventually), some new phase will follow. Emotions may feel as though they are flooding your thoughts. Illness and diagnosis certainly take us by surprise, but over time it will become more normal and you will again feel a measure of control.

Romeo: Courage, man; the hurt cannot be much.

Mercutio: No, 'tis not so deep as a well, nor so
          wide as a church-door;
          but 'tis enough, 'twill serve.
                                    Shakespeare

It is not always easy to tell family and friends how you are feeling, especially when you want to say you would rather be alone. There is nothing wrong, but there is a lot that's right about saying, "Ouch," when it is time to let others know you are uncomfortable.

Susan Abeyta has definite feelings about how and when to say, "Ouch. Leave me alone." The "please" is clearly optional.

"This [chronic illness] is a tragedy that befalls people, like getting hit by a car or having your baby die. You can't make it not happen. You can't not care that it happened. You get to feel bad because there is so much in our society today that says, 'Have a positive attitude.'

"No. I have cancer, thank you. I get to feel bad. You go have a positive attitude.

"When I didn't have cancer, I had a positive attitude. Then, when I'm done feeling bad, I'll have a positive attitude. And then tomorrow I'll feel bad again. And then I'll have a positive attitude again. I have to do that for however long I have to do this.

"Most people have said I do have a positive attitude: 'Oh, you're doing so wonderfully. I'm sure everything's going to be just fine.' You feel really stupid. What you want to say is, 'Wait a minute. I have cancer. I'm not doing well.'"

"There was the sense they were minimizing it. Like people say to people at a funeral, 'Oh, you're taking things so well.' Bullshit. There's a tremendous amount of pain."

When you don't feel well, what do you do? Do you keep it to yourself or tell others? Do you want feedback or would you prefer to be heard and get no response? Do you want company or isolation? Would you like to take a walk or read a book?

Would you like a back rub or kiss? Would you like to be busy doing something in the house or out of the house? Do you, like Susan Abeyta, want people to be absolutely honest or to shut up?

These seem like simple questions, but they are not. The person with a chronic physical problem struggles with all aspects of how to cope and how to respond. The additional problem is that nobody around is likely to have any idea of what should be done.

There are no foolproof guidelines, nor rules describing how to help someone with a cyclic, chronic illness. Your friends and family are probably confused and bewildered about how to respond to you when you don't feel well. This is especially pronounced if you have been recently diagnosed (see Chapter 14). The scene is ripe for miscommunication (see Chapter 17).

"No one around you can take away the pain or the fact that you have to deal with it," says Mary Alice Kerr. "But surrounding yourself with people who support you helps. If you're always having to explain yourself to somebody, you're wasting energy in a place that it doesn't need to be, because it takes so much concentration just trying to take care of yourself."

The fact is that nobody knows what is soothing for an individual without asking. One person may require soft, quiet words. For others, an hour or two of being completely alone is appropriate. For still others, a show of physical affection or a sympathetic ear can prove to be effective. And sometimes, the feelings are mixed and paradoxical.

Allan Pike reflects on his liver transplant hospitalization: "Through the whole thing, it was really the support of people and friends that made it doable, even though at times I wanted to get rid of them and say, 'Leave me alone.'

"I tend to retreat from the world and just fight it inside—just me and the force of will. I tell myself, 'I'm going to overcome this by myself. Don't bother me.' But it was very important for me to have my family there. I really did miss them when they weren't there. I got very alone."

How do you want to be treated? Think about that for a moment. What has happened in the past in the company of others that made you angry? Frustrated? Relaxed? Calmed? Putting it in chart form can give you a chance to gain some perspective.

When I am not feeling well, I would like reactions from (list five important people):

1. _____

2. _____

3. _____

4. _____

5. _____

I would like (name of person 1) to do the following kinds of things when I feel bad:

I would like (name of person 2) to do the following kinds of things when I feel bad:

I would like (name of person 3) to do the following kinds of things when I feel bad:

I would like (name of person 4) to do the following kinds of things when I feel bad:

I would like (name of person 5) to do the following kinds of things when I feel bad:

Now that you have thought about what kind of reaction you would like ("no reaction" is an acceptable answer), let's think about how you want to communicate about your physical state.

How do you usually act when you don't feel well? There is a broad range of responses to this question. People vary greatly in the way they communicate to others what is happening internally. Some have an easy time sharing their physical experiences. Others have a very difficult time.

Michelle Frank, 44, stubs her toe on the couch and is able to tell every detail of the event to her husband. She describes what led up to the injury, how badly it hurt, and even shows him the bruise. She invites his attention and sympathy, and both of them feel better. He dashes off to get ice and then rubs her foot. The experience bonds them.

Lisa Grant, 54, has chemotherapy. She has great fears about cancer and is grieving the results of a hysterectomy. She stoically goes through the treatments, experiencing the usual nausea and weakness. She feels incapacitated for weeks and needs the help of friends to manage on a daily basis. She doesn't discuss her feelings with anyone and is very uncomfortable when her friends and husband help out. She feels best when she is alone and sighs in relief as they leave her room.

Which is correct?

Both, of course. As we pointed out earlier, there are no rules about how, when, or with whom we share our woes. This is a highly personal issue and it cannot be mandated by others. The struggle over these decisions is ongoing. Because of the sporadic nature of the discomfort and the resulting emotional mood, whom you would like to have with you, or whom you don't want around you, can change in the course of several hours.

"I feel strongly that it is my responsibility to inform others about the way I want them to behave around me," Sandra McCollum says. "I have finally realized that people cannot be expected to understand how I feel if I don't make my wishes known. The biggest help that another person can offer is to ask me what I want or can do, or to encourage me in a goal, rather than try to tell me what I should do or have to do."

It is obvious that there is no way to get what you want, or prevent what you don't want, unless you figure out a way to let others know what is necessary for you. As Mick Jagger reminds us, albeit in another context, "You can't always get what you want. But try hard enough, and you may just get what you need."

Chapter Exercise

Ouch Meter

You have to let people know where in the cycle of illness or discomfort you are. How about an Ouch Meter for that purpose? Think of the Ouch Meter as a communication device with a six-point scale. It ranges from feeling well on one extreme to feeling so bad that no interaction is advisable.

Calibrating the Ouch Meter has to be done individually and in any way you like. Let's say you are a person who likes personal interaction even when you are ill and in discomfort. Your Ouch Meter might look like the one below. Remember, once you and your spouse or companion know the "code" (for example, use number),it can be communicated quickly in a restaurant, at a party, or elsewhere around other people.

With friends or others not familiar with the calibrations, it is a simple gesture for you to locate where you are on the Ouch Meter and convey the information to them, as necessary. In addition, calibrating the Ouch Meter to your own needs and cycles helps you focus on the sometimes subtle differences associated with your distress—a familiarity that engenders additional control and perspective.

Sample Ouch Meter

Code	Message
1 —	I feel great; let's play.
2 —	I'm a little under the weather and I'm having a few rough moments. Let me tell you about it.
3 —	Things are acting up. I need to talk. I'll probably be okay.
4 —	I feel bad. I'm struggling. Just stay nea me. I'll try to talk. But I might ask you to leave me alone.
5 —	I feel terrible. I must retreat. Leave me alone.

16. Mutual Caring

The wheel is come full circle.
Shakespeare

This chapter touches on a ticklish problem. It asks you to consider the question of how well you care for, protect, and nurture the people who care about you. Other chapters have examined ways to improve how you attend to yourself. Now it is time to look in a different direction. It is time to look around and see if you may be coping in a way that is hurting the ones you love, and how you might change that.

A gentle warning: The topic in this chapter is especially hard to address because it invites you to engage in self-criticism and personal assessment. And it taps into your deepest feelings about the ones you love.

Is your coping style hurting your family members and friends? The people around you may never ask this question out loud or discuss it with you directly.

We have been taught to believe that it is taboo to complain about our own emotional discomfort to a person in physical distress. It is almost as if we are psychically sworn to silence. There are other reasons caregivers may be reluctant to complain about themselves.

1. They may try not to think about it because it evokes strong, threatening, or anxious feelings. ("There's no point in thinking about something you can't change.")

2. They are focusing their energies on making things more comfortable for you right now. (This keeps them busy and active but encourages the repression or burying of negative feelings.)

3. They know that revealing unpleasant feelings may lead to a confrontation, and this is frightening. ("Anger might make her sicker and then I'd be responsible. Besides, what if we exchange ugly words. She never takes my advice, anyway.")

Despite the caregiver's silence, it is in your best emotional and physical interest to make sure others feel you are a useful and positive influence in their lives. If they feel good about you and act accordingly, you will feel good and act accordingly about them. Simply, and perhaps a bit crudely, put: The capacity to care for others is an excellent insurance policy for the future of the relationship, whether you are chronically ill or not.

The process is not easy. And, as Karen Stone has discovered, it takes "about a couple of years of adjusting, learning, growing, and adjusting some more. It's hard to continually rise above the struggles and reach out." But, she says, the outcome can be fulfilling.

"The successes are small and very insignificant. But every time we care, every time we flex our muscles, every time we reach out, we grow. And in this, our quality of life improves."

Rebecca Steinberg's dilemma was of a different kind.

"My children initially were in denial. They didn't want to talk about it, they didn't want to deal with it, and I had to take them by the scruff of the neck and shake them and say, 'This is what we're dealing with and we're going to talk about it and we're not going to pretend it isn't there.'

"They didn't want to deal with it. Nobody wants to think they're losing their mother, I guess. So I had to force them to deal with it. And what they all said was, 'Oh, you're so strong. We know you're going to be fine. We know that you're not going to let this kill you.'

"But there were times when I needed to talk about it and not have them change the subject when I did."

The capacity to care is defined as the "ability to form friendly and loving bonds with others with a minimum of inappropriate hostility and the ability to sustain the relationship over a period of time with little mutual exchange of hostility."

In short, caring is a blend of friendship and love given to another person over a long period with a minimal amount of anger exchanged. This task becomes even harder if you have a chronic physical problem. But it can be done.

"I have been the aggravation—and much worse—of friends, family, and physicians," Sandra McCollum declares. "I admit I'm stubborn, certain that my lifestyle is right, obstinate about following orders that take away my control, and generally very single-minded about doing what I think is best for me.

"I do, however, try to consider what it is like to try to deal with or live with me. I have watched enough suffering in others to know that in many ways it is easier to be the person working through the disease. There is, unfortunately, not much to be said for watching a loved one suffer. Perhaps those who must stand by are the ones who truly deserve sainthood. Family members desperately need attention and understanding from caregivers."

Mary Alice Kerr has become "more compassionate" as a result of her experiences. "My understanding of family and friends has grown a lot."

Going through a terrible medical ordeal can change one's perspective. It did for Allan Pike, a physician specializing in pulmonary medicine.

"I'm much more open now," he says. "I've become more accepting of other people's flaws. I was always very critical of people, always looking for the perfect person.

"I try to be nice to people, despite my problems, and not get angry or frustrated. I've learned that I really do need people. I enjoy people a lot more than I did."

We know that chronic and acute stress can frequently interfere with the degree to which one person can successfully attend to another person. Illness tends to make us feel helpless and angry. That is how we felt as children when we found that the world occasionally frustrated some of our needs. Back then, important things seemed to occur with little or no predictability.

Illness consciously or unconsciously brings back old memories, special images, and behavior patterns. Without realizing it, we recall how our parents took care of us and how they seemed to feel as they did so. We remember how we experienced vulnerability.

In some cases our vulnerability brought out the best

behaviors in our parents and ourselves. Some people report that they grew immensely in their emotional ability to feel when their mother or father helped them through a rough time. Others report that illness or stress made everyone in the family angry, selfish, or depressed.

Like childhood, when life often was unpredictable and without clear explanations ("Don't ask why" "Because I said so, that's why"), a physical disability evokes confusion and subjective feelings of unfair suffering. Some people are able to look at their disability while maintaining a philosophical perspective. They see it as part of the human condition—nothing personal.

Most of us are not like that. We feel harassed by our physical stress. We may feel victimized, persecuted, and even experience a sense of abandonment as our body fails us. All these feelings, and more, reawaken childhood fantasies and memories, and whether we know it or not we begin to act as we did as children in relation to important parental figures. The old pattern that may erupt is highly self-oriented and does not give us room to listen, to empathize, to be sensitive.

Louise Young, 45, is married. She has arthritis and is struggling with her decreasing motor skills. She has dressed with great care and is going out for dinner with her husband. She wants to navigate the wheelchair to get out the door, something she has done previously with varying degrees of success.

Her husband is standing by and anticipating a potential problem. He asks if she might wait as he opens the door.

"I'd rather do it myself," she says, a bit irritated.

He quietly backs off. She knows she's done it before; why can't she do it this time? The chronic uncertainty of knowing when, or if, the disease's fluctuating symptoms will allow an activity from moment to moment makes for a ready flashpoint of anger. She crashes into the door frame and navigates back.

She tries once more before the pain and lack of agility become unbearable. She sits motionless in the chair, tears streaming down her face, unable even to leave the scene of frustration and despair. Her husband is left sad and confused. Who is the source of the problem here?

To consider this, you have to accept one important assumption about caring: Everyone is equal in importance. The pleasure, sadness, hopes, and disappointments of one person are as important as those of another.

So if we assess the quality of Louise's caring, we have to wonder. The angry outburst, her refusal of help, her neglect of the consequences of her explosion on her husband, all reflect a selfishness. She did it herself, but both paid for that decision. She was unable to attend to her spouse's distress, and it was as important to him as his was to her. Her anger and false independence ruined the beginning of a potentially intimate evening.

Here's another example. John Kesseling, a 52-year-old schoolteacher, arrives home with his back in pain. He enters the house and will talk to no one. He is furious that his chronic back problems have returned, and he is beginning to sulk.

He belligerently comes to the dinner table; the family can cut the tension with the proverbial butter knife. He yells at his son for dropping his fork and eating too fast.

(Actually, you can easily understand that his son might want to eat quickly to get away from the tense table.)

His wife signals the children to be extra quiet and not to disturb Dad because he is not feeling well. They have certainly heard that before. Clearly, John is not behaving in a caring fashion. In fact, he is a downright pain himself—for everyone. Implicit in his behavior, and a factor in stirring up family resentment, is the message that his distress is greater and more important than the psychological needs of everyone else in the household.

One final example. Julie Sheridan, 46, returns home from work with chest pain. A cardiac patient, she takes some nitroglycerin as she anxiously enters the living room. She goes up to her bedroom and starts to bark out orders to her husband and college-age son, who is home for the holidays.

She demands her purse be brought, and then her book that's on the kitchen counter. She asks for tea and again calls out to her husband with another request. "Call my mother and tell her I'm not feeling well."

She angrily hisses at her son to lower his stereo. Within seconds, the entire mood of the house has changed. She has forgotten the needs of the family. If this happens often enough, they will feel angry at her and guilty about resenting her behavior—if they don't already.

As you can see, people under physical stress show noncaring behavior in a number of ways. They can be:

1. *Selfish about needs and plans.* They don't consider the needs or feelings of the spouse or other family members.

2. *Oblivious to the plans and agenda of others.* They operate in their own world of pain, discomfort, and relief, with little awareness of what others feel.

3. *Openly hostile.* They attack, suspect, and accuse family members of being unconcerned or are overly critical.

4. *Sarcastic.* They use anger cloaked in humor to poke at and put down others so they too feel vulnerable.

5. *Helpless.* They seem to be even more unable to move and respond than one would expect with those particular physical problems. They seem to bathe in passivity ("You decide for me").

6. *Angry about the illness.* They express endless fury at life, at nature, at doctors. Their anger becomes an intrusion in any intimate situation.

7. *Manipulative.* They use subtle manipulations to get what they want.

8. *Insatiable.* They need more affection, attention, care, and feedback than is possible. Their family feels like a guilty, dried-up spring.

9. *Antisocial.* With quiet irritation, they become a stumbling block for any family entertaining. ("I can't have my friends over when Dad just sits there and won't talk or look up").

10. *Overly sensitive.* They seem to be waiting for further injury from those around them. Any comment causes an unusually intense reaction. Everyone must handle them with kid gloves.

11. *Secretive.* They won't talk about what is happening. Their secret becomes a powerful weapon that evokes more questions and causes much confusion.

These are only a few possibilities. Unfortunately, the list is much longer. We can hurt the people around us with silence, small gestures, neglect, and other subtle reactions.

If you look at the list and say, "This has nothing to do with me," or, "Yes, that fits, but I'm not that bad," or, "I'm sick. Of course I'm grumpy and angry and insensitive. Who wouldn't be?"—hold on. You and your behavior are profoundly important to everyone around you.

Mary Alice Kerr's reaction to that discovery is instructive.

"I had friends who cared so much about me that they would cry. One of the reasons I hate [my condition] is it hurts other people so much. So many times people say, 'It's not your fault, there's nothing you can do.' I just hate seeing them hurting because of me, but that's probably one of the most touching things that's happened to me."

Because Allan Pike is both a professional caregiver and a sufferer of chronic illness, his words resonate on several levels. His personal medical experience has altered his perspective about those he treats.

"I feel sympathetic toward them. I try to spend more

time with them. I say, 'Hey, listen. I know how you're feeling. I was in a situation where I was near death. I was told I had only so many years to live. Everyone's different. I beat the odds and you may beat the odds, too.'

"Sometimes it means something to them that their doctor has been sick, too, and that he understands them."

Think about how much joy, nurturing, and encouragement you give to those around you. If you are able to recognize that this may be a weak spot, then you already are on your way. If you look at the list presented here and feel a small twinge of discomfort, then you're probably about to make some progress. For only when we can be introspective and try to observe objectively are we able to consider difficult and complex problems that are part of our lives.

What if, as you read over the list, you say, "Every one of these applies to me. I have been terrible and inhumane. I cannot possibly make up for what I have done"? If this is your response, you are probably absorbing too much blame. Slow down and reread the list. Pick the area that is your most obvious flaw and begin there.

Chapter Exercise

Nourishing the Family

Look through the 11 items described earlier (pages 187-189), and spend a few minutes thinking about which ones may apply to you. It is important to try to be as frank and honest as possible. This is, after all, for your consideration, not anyone else's. After each item, put a check mark in the appropriate column.

	Applies	Doesn't Apply	Rating
1. Selfish about needs/plans of others			
2. Oblivious to plans/agenda			
3. Openly hostile			
4. Sarcastic			
5. Helpless			
6. Angry			
7. Manipulative			
8. Insatiable			
9. Antisocial			
10. Overly Sensitive			
11. Secretive			

Now rate whether the item is one that occurs

    0 — Never
    1 — Seldom
    2 — Sometimes
    3 — Frequently
    4 — Almost always

How Can You Change?

Review the scored items and think about what it would take for you to change them. You can communicate in many ways. While these may be obvious, we may tend to overlook them in the course of our daily activities. They are all worth remembering:

- Words (e.g., telling someone you miss them)
- Gestures (e.g., hugs, a smile)
- Listening (e.g., asking about somebody's day)
- Behavior (e.g., offering to help, bringing home a surprise)

Start to plan how you can do this. Make a list of things you usually do to indicate that you care.

1.

2.

3.

4.

5.

6.

7.

8.

9.

10.

Now make a list of things you would like to do to show how much you care for a variety of acquaintances. You may need a separate list for each important person. (See Helping Out, page 251, for more ideas.)

Spouse/Companion
    1.
    2.
    3.

Child
    1.
    2.
    3.

Child
    1.
    2.
    3.

Friend
    1.
    2.
    3.

Colleague, other. etc.
    1.
    2.
    3.

> By speaking of our misfortunes we
> often relieve them.
>
> **Pierre Corneille**

People with a chronic illness or disability have a trio of disturbing feelings lurking in the shadows of their emotional lives. Others may come and go, but these three are universal. Acknowledging their presence is helpful to all concerned.

Anger, anxiety, and depression are emotions found in all of us. They are probably not new to you.

These uninvited visitors intrude upon your life. They make your efforts to cope more difficult. As with other intrusions, they are more easily managed if recognized and identified. If they are not accepted, they can cause subtle, unconscious, indirect, and covert damage.

Anxiety

Chronic symptoms overwhelm because you cannot make them go away. You cannot always control them.

Anxiety is the granddaddy of all emotions. Whenever we feel out of control and threatened, anxiety emerges. You may feel nervous, shaky, ill-at-ease. Bodily symptoms provide cues: shortness of breath, rapid breathing, tingling sensations in fingers and toes, intestinal discomfort, numbness, chest pain, "butterflies" in the stomach, diarrhea or constipation, muscle cramps, sweating, dizziness. All these are messages from the autonomic nervous system telling us that we are overwhelmed.

Anger

Anger is an extreme protest that your psyche makes. It usually surfaces in people who have been physically or emotionally attacked or injured. Its message is: Life has not been fair. People who are burdened with chronic illness often feel persecuted and unlucky. Sensitive to their frustration, they feel an internal sense of insult. Anger is a particularly focused reaction.

Anger is not always directed at others. Frequently, people express anger, verbally or physically, toward themselves. While the psychological expression of anger cannot be measured with precision, it is possible to indicate on a scale the progressively intense gradient of its expression, according to Dr. David Landau.

At one extreme, passive anger may be expressed by neglect of one's own body (e.g., not taking prescribed medication, being withdrawn and noncommunicative).

Further along is verbal abuse, which is characterized by insults and sarcasm. ("You think you know more than the doctor?") Verbal threats are the next notch on the scale. ("If you don't leave me alone, I'm leaving.") Beyond this point, the anger gradient goes from physical threat ("I'll kick your ass"), to aggressive (breaking and throwing objects), and, finally, to violent (striking others). It looks like this:

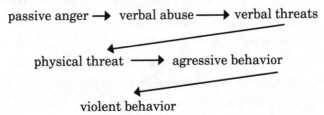

passive anger → verbal abuse → verbal threats

physical threat → agressive behavior

violent behavior

Obviously, not all periods of anger are the same. We vary greatly in the patterns of anger we feel and express. Similarly, anger can be contained in a variety of ways, including intense physical activity (e.g., running, chopping wood) or building things, cleaning, or playing a musical instrument.

It is again important to note that sharing feelings significantly decreases anger. Having someone to talk to has proven to be a significant outlet for pent-up fury and can also serve as an active pressure-release valve. Illness is frustrating. Words can ease the tension.

Depression

If you are giving up skills and wellness that you once took for granted or thought you would have forever, you are going to experience sadness and depression. Depression is characterized by a sense of loss and a feeling of flatness or emptiness about life.

People who are experiencing depression report that they feel helpless and hopeless. Their self-esteem is low and they have difficulty participating in virtually any activity. Things that brought pleasure in the past, no longer do. Eating and sleeping patterns are disrupted and a change in sexual appetite occurs. Sometimes, because life has lost its joy for them, depressed individuals report fantasies or thoughts about dying.

You will have to wait to see if the depression lifts, or force yourself to become involved in life around you. Medications are available that can help you deal with depression, but talking and communicating may be the best method of lifting the sense of dread.

The message should be clear by now: Sharing your experiences with someone else increases your chances of feeling better, whether you are experiencing anger, anxiety, or depression.

In his early work, Freud spoke about strangulated affect—feelings that are buried or not expressed. Translated, this means that the chronic illness sufferer who buries feelings below the surface ends by carrying a double burden.

First, energy is required to cope with the illness. Second, energy is used to keep the feelings repressed. Because illness in any form is stressful, there is no way to eliminate the struggles of coping. But that is no reason to bear the extra weight of holding down hidden feelings. If you share them, you will feel considerable relief. Learning to express yourself may decrease stress sufficiently to improve your life.

Who are your potential listeners? We list 10 choices for you in the following pages. Some are obvious and familiar, others may be new, and still others you may already have tried. But all bring something different, something unique in either perspective or understanding, to their potential role of listener.

While it is important to consider how emotionally comfortable you feel speaking with a particular person, it is also a good idea to think about the substance, or content, that person brings to the role of listener. Do you want a passive listener who remains silent when you talk? Or do you prefer someone who has specific advice to offer? Are you worried about exposing your emotions to someone who may not be entirely sympathetic to your problems? Or does a combination of listeners appeal to you, a smorgasboard of simpaticos from which you can choose depending on your mood and immediate needs?

1. Your doctor.

If you are fortunate, you have a doctor who is both a competent practitioner and an empathic and patient listener, someone who not only knows and understands the impact of your illness or disability, but is interested in its effect on the totality of your life. This doctor also manages to leave time to share a discussion before, during, or after the examination or treatment.

If you have a doctor like this, the next step is yours. Be ready to take a chance and tell your doctor about anything that has been frightening, upsetting, and frustrating you. If it makes you feel more at ease, have notes prepared (see Chapter 4).

If you lose control, that is okay. Tears are acceptable, as well as curses and confusion. All feelings are reasonable for someone who is sick.

Allan Pike, himself a physician, learned firsthand, as a patient, what patients should expect, even demand, from their doctors. Some of this surprised him. Operated on in a big, busy teaching hospital/medical center, he got lost in the shuffle.

"I never even saw the guys who did the operation," he recalls. "I didn't know who to thank. I didn't know who to be angry with."

He remembers a nurse informing him rather abruptly that his doctor had ordered a biopsy. She told him to sign the release for permission to proceed. He told her in no uncertain terms that he would not agree to the biopsy unless he first got more information directly from an attending faculty member.

"I just put up a stink. I was afraid to put it up. I didn't want people to get mad at me. That was the thing that made me the maddest, the thing I talked to people about when I came back to work—how mad I was that people didn't talk to me and involve me."

Now, he tries to give his patients "the whole scoop." At the same time, he has also come to recognize that a lot of people don't want the whole story. "I've pissed off a lot of people—'Oh, you upset my wife so badly.' All I'm trying to do is lay out the fact that I think you need to know as much as I know about things and try not to overwhelm people with technical information.

"But you need to know what the deal is. You need to know what your options are, what the complications are. I spend a lot of time with people and it pays off. But it is amazing that there are people who don't want to know."

2. The nurse.

The nurse travels by the doctor's side through the land of the suffering. Nurses often know important details about each patient's life. They are trained to pick up on subtle personal issues. Often, they are more accessible and receptive than the doctor.

3. Your spouse or companion.

This choice is perfect in terms of availability and familiarity. But tough problems can arise. Issues of confidentiality, hurt feelings, and misunderstood emotions need to be addressed. Discussing intimate topics can elicit old unresolved conflicts. However, it is likely that no one knows you as well as your spouse or companion does.

4. Your family.

The word *family* includes a wide array of people, including those within and outside your immediate household. Often, we find that our family members possess more resources than we expect. People who care about you appreciate having an opportunity to listen to your concerns. Even children can be good listeners if they're not required to sit still for too long and if they get a chance to share their own complaints about life.

5. Your friends.

Most of our friendships are based on the mutual sharing of pleasures or interests. In addition, friendships often require that both parties are equally able to listen and talk. If you talk about your disability and your friend does not reciprocate by sharing difficulties, the relationship may be derailed. Friendships that permit room to share troubles tend to last for a long time and these friendships deepen as we age.

Karen Stone asked her friend Pat Weber to write an article for *Copability*, Karen's newly launched newsletter. Here is what Pat wrote:

"When Karen first asked me to be guest writer . . . , my mind filled with experiences she and I had shared during her own personal battle. Like the time, on a particularly shaky day, I had offered to assist her crossing the parking lot to the car. I had stumbled in my 'fashion-able' high heels, and we ended up leaning against the car, laughing at who was really helping who. Laughing.

"Or the time, after months of knowing something was wrong, but waiting patiently for Karen to find the right time to tell me, the right time to break the news to me, a mere friend, that she had M.S. The aching and grief I felt for her, knowing full well she had the same aching and grief to a much greater degree. Or the evening I forced myself to face what she was facing, knowing I couldn't ignore it. Putting myself in her shoes. The crying.

"The laughter and the tears. That's what being on the other side is all about. Being able to be fully honest with someone afflicted—to tell them of your sorrow, your grief. To laugh with them at life's incongruities and ironies, like attempting to aid someone and receiving aid from them instead.

"The joys of watching small progress. The sorrow of losing a battle. The amazement at watching someone gain spiritual strength from a physical deficit. The learning to love someone fully—truly love someone, for what they are, not for what you see.

"My relationship with Karen is ever growing. I learn more and more from her about strength. Stick-to-it-iveness. Or, in Karen's words: piss 'n vinegar. . . .

"The best advice I can give to someone who has a disability, handicap, or whatever label . . . , is this: Be all you can to those 'on the other side.' Be all you are—give of yourself. And, let them give of themselves. Let them love you. Be honest with them and let them be honest with you. Something beautiful develops. Every time."

6. Others with physical problems.

In the vast number of other people with physical problems, we find an emotional gold mine. The easiest place to locate others with similar coping needs is, of course, through the foundation, agency, or local chapter associated with your particular illness or disability. One interesting option in this context, one that can give you a different but very useful perspective, is to contact the local chapter representing a chronic illness different from yours. Talking about similar coping problems can be bracing and eye-opening.

"When you're out there by yourself, you want to talk to people you can relate to, so I sought it out," Rebecca Steinberg says of the support group she attended."It serves a real important community function."

7. Professional help.

There are many ways to make contact and share problems with people who are trained to listen to your struggles and to help you with them. This includes the wide world of counselors, ministers, social workers, psychologists, and psychiatrists. The advantages of using a professional listener is that your conversation will remain confidential, there is likely to be little superficial advice given (as is sometimes the case with friends and family), and it can be arranged and planned.

Importantly, talking to a professional will help you acknowledge your own pain as a real issue, and your good coping skills will be noticed and explored. You also will not have to fear breaking down. Professionals know the importance of letting go emotionally and aren't put off by it.

The negative part is that you will have to be ready to talk to someone you don't know, payment is often required (you should discuss sliding scale fees and alternative payment schedules), and you and the professional must feel comfortable with each other (forming the "therapeutic bond").

Therapy groups are also available. These usually have a leader and people participating with similar and different problems. The cost of these sessions is often a quarter or third of individual therapy, and the environment is emotionally safe.

8. Informal helpers.

There are people to talk to who have no formal therapeutic credentials, nor are they fellow sufferers. These are the people with whom you regularly interact on a one-to-one basis for some service or social reason. They include your barber or hairdresser, teachers, bartenders, mentors, housekeepers, alternative healers, sports partners, and very special clerks at stores you frequent.

You can easily make up your own list. Individuals with chronic illness often have learned to talk briefly but sincerely to these almost invisible but important members of their psychological community.

Often, all it takes is for you to share part of the truth when someone asks "How are you doing?"—instead of keeping up the facade.

9. Write.

Another way to express feelings is to write them down.

Some people find writing a letter—to yourself or to someone you know and care about—or a journal gives them a way to express themselves at a pace that is controlled and doesn't require immediate comment or feedback from someone sitting nearby.

The recipient of a letter can likewise respond to it at a comfortable pace. It can be read in parts and it can be answered in depth or briefly. Try it.

Journal writing is, of course, more private (see Chapter 2). But its usefulness lies in the fact that you express every detail of your struggle. Tears, screams, joys, and fury can be "talked" about in a journal without any worry of disapproval, anger, guilt or some other negative reaction on the part of anyone else. As you can see, it is helpful and healthy to get those words out any way you can.

10. How about listening?

You have just read all the reasons for talking, but you still find it too difficult and embarrassing to reveal your feelings to someone else. Maybe some other time.

We have another alternative for you. Many people report that if they listen to someone else who is struggling, some of their own feelings are released. We hear other people talk about their pain and we identify with them and their problems. We understand what they are experiencing unconsciously. We sympathize and offer them solace.

We also know that at that moment, we are detached and separate from their problem. Somehow there is safety and relief in that knowledge. Our own problem suddenly becomes different, less intense, and perhaps more in our control in contrast to their difficulties. We end our listening feeling better, with a changed perspective.

To start, you can volunteer to listen to patients with problems similar to yours. For example, you can work at the local hospital or at a crisis center for one or two hours a week.

You can answer phones at an agency and you can tell your doctor or nurse that you would like to help others who have similar problems. Volunteering to listen benefits everyone involved. After a while, you may begin to feel comfortable enough to think about reversing the process. When that happens, go over the above list again and make your choice.

Chapter Exercise

So You Want To Talk?

We have offered several techniques and locales to facilitate the expression of your feelings about your struggles. The trick is to find the one that's right for you.

Do not let false pride or shyness keep you from talking about emotions or venting. Do not let individual rejections stop you from your determined hunt for the perfect listener.

Work on expressing yourself regularly so you don't try to blurt out everything at once. Saying too much can be frightening and frustrating. Good novelists know how to lay out a story gradually. Not everything is revealed in the first chapter. While we don't necessarily expect you to be the next Stephen King, it is nonetheless important to keep in mind that the patient, committed listener will allow you time to tell your story.

Whom Do You Trust?

Step I.—List six people who fit into the listener categories described above (pages 199-205. After the name of each person, write the three strengths they have as a listener. Then write three weaknesses they have as listeners. For example,

Harry

   Brother-in-law—Family

   Strength   1. Patient

          2. Quiet

          3. Good listener

   Weakness   1. No feedback

          2. Might tell his wife

          3. Too busy

Louise

   Neighbor/Friend

   Strength   1. Empathic

          2. Has had similar problem

          3. Likes sharing feelings

Weakness 1. Never alone for long

2. Too busy

3. Has short attention span

(Remember to include doctor, nurse, and casual acquaintances as well as family and friends. Take your time and think about it carefully.)

Name	Relationship	Strength	Weakness
1. _____ _____		1. _____ 2. _____ 3. _____	1. _____ 2. _____ 3. _____
2. _____ _____		1. _____ 2. _____ 3. _____	1. _____ 2. _____ 3. _____
3. _____ _____		1. _____ 2. _____ 3. _____	1. _____ 2. _____ 3. _____
4. _____ _____		1. _____ 2. _____ 3. _____	1. _____ 2. _____ 3. _____
5. _____ _____		1. _____ 2. _____ 3. _____	1. _____ 2. _____ 3. _____
6. _____ _____		1. _____ 2. _____ 3. _____	1. _____ 2. _____ 3. _____

Step II.—Next, start checking the usefulness of your list. Try one or two people and see if you are on target. You can be clear with them that you have a lot on your mind and would like to talk. Or you can just bring up matters that are bothering you without directly stating why you are talking to them. Keep track of the reactions, and your feelings, and write them down on the chart below.

Name of listener of listener	Reactions	How you felt
1. _____	_____	_____
2. _____	_____	_____
3. _____	_____	_____

Step III .—What is hard for you to talk about? At this point, it is a good idea to write down those aspects of your physical problems that are difficult to share with others. Perhaps they have to do with basic bodily functions, or feelings. Do not be surprised if shame makes it to the censored list.

The reason this list is important is that it may help you think about what would be good to share and what you do not choose to share. Making things conscious puts you in the driver's seat—and in control.

Some areas that are threatening and hard to talk about:

- Shame (e.g., losing bladder control)
- Dying (e.g., brings up bad memories)
- Control (e.g., losing self-control in public)
- Emotions (e.g., worrying about going crazy, laughing too hard)
- Self-esteem (e.g., my problems aren't worth bothering anyone about)
- Exposure (e.g., I don't want to be put in a position of vulnerability; I've been hurt enough)

Every gaudy color
Is a bit of truth
Nathalia Crane

Your body holds astounding gifts that provide you with many possibilities for all kinds of sensory experiences. When you have a chronic disability, you tend to think more negatively than positively. The body becomes associated with bad experiences. In actuality, the mind can shift in its focus.

We are highly suggestible creatures, and the anticipation of physical stress alone can keep us hopping mentally and emotionally. We forget that each sense—touch, sight, smell, hearing, taste—is both an immediate and potential source of stimulation and pleasure. For the chronically ill, it is sometimes hard to remember that pleasure as well as pain is a birthright of the human condition.

It is helpful, first, to return to the idealized pictures of childhood. Many of the delights of growing up are sensory. Parents put the child in a soft crib and cradle. They monitor lighting to be gentle, not harsh. They surround the infant with mobiles and little toys that the baby learns to push, pull, and manipulate. Music comes out of a stuffed toy and gentle words and laughter come from caretakers. The taste of warm milk soothes and comforts.

The child also knows about stressful times. When the youngster is hungry, thirsty, wet, sleepy, sick, or fatigued, she experiences what it is like to be out of control and to feel hurt.

As we reach adulthood, we bring our own unique cluster of sensory experiences along with us. The task of seeking sensual stimulation and protection from noxious stimuli is then placed upon our shoulders. By now, we have learned that each of our senses can provide meaningful comfort, distraction, and renewal. The responsibility for making the appropriate choices is yours.

Sight

What visual images make you feel happy and relaxed? If you can't come up with an answer right away, take a few moments to think about it. List five visual experiences that make you smile or feel content.

1.

2.

3.

4.

5.

This is a starting list. It is important to continue adding to it. The following will help you recall images that bring you pleasure.

Many people associate natural beauty with enjoyment. Animals, nature scenes, open spaces, beaches, mountains, flowers. The folks who make those large mural landscape wallpapers know this. Some of the back-drops we see on TV shows serve the same purpose. Perhaps, as you read this, pictures of pleasant associa-tions—vacation scenes, city scenes with crowds of people, a recent family reunion, time alone with a mountain view—come to mind.

For some, designs, shapes, and patterns are pleas-ing to the eye. Maybe there are famous people whose picture or statue you like to look at. Perhaps painting or artwork appeals to you. Or there may be colors that you find especially restful or appealing.

Interior decorators and commercial office space de-signers have known for years that certain colors excite or calm or depress. Some people actively seek out visual input for changes in mood.

Often we see that people who don't feel well give up possibilities. They don't take the opportunity to put up pictures. They pay no attention to lighting. They ignore colors. They leave their favorite items out of sight and find themselves left in bare surroundings with no reflection of the healthiest parts of themselves. Sometimes they allow the people around them to decide what they want, and passively forfeit all choices.

The message, as always, is to fight to overcome passivity. It takes very little to have pleasant visual stimulation around you. Again, we can take a leaf from the pages of childhood.

Infants are pleasurably stimulated by colorful mo-biles. The early recognition of their parents' faces is a landmark development in the formation of trust and predictability in their world. The first tacking of a poster to the bedroom wall marks the beginning of a child's taking on a new identity. For an adolescent, the idol in a wall poster gazing, staring, or glaring back is a real reminder of selfhood.

You may need your own reminder. Get to work and begin to design a room of your fantasies. Have a little fun with this. A large pad of paper and a pen, or even a box of crayons, might help you. A few magazines with material that reflects your interests will encourage inspiration.

If you like sports, start to put some of that in your "viewing" plan. The same goes for fine art, furniture of your favorite historical period, literary interests, botanical gardens (or a neighbor's backyard rose bush display), cultural and museum exhibits, church or temple interiors, crowds at sporting events. Fashion, architecture (out on the street or in a pictorial essay), even a choice of beautiful Oriental starkness is fine, if you choose it. Photos and books with favorite scenes are nice to have handy; pull them out and look at them when you like.

It is important to know that visual stimulation can be uplifting. Even people-watching can be fun! The more you notice, the more familiar surroundings seem to become stimulating.

Preparing to make changes can be threatening. What if you paint a room blue and it looks terrible? What if you get a new poster, picture, or photograph, and it looks lousy on the wall? Remember, your physical problems are a source of concern a good deal of the time. If you don't like what you've created, try again! So what if it takes 5 or 10 or 20 trials to get the image you want? Just as the teenager risks ridicule in putting up the first poster, you have to take risks, too.

Auditory Stimulation

Your ears know sounds that are pleasing and displeasing. There are sounds that make people relax almost instantly, such as water running in a brook, birds twittering in a forest, soft, quiet rain, ocean breakers against the shore, a song, silence. A favorite sound can be brought into your living room via tape.

Back in the days of radio, many people planned their entire week so they could hear the voices of their favorite entertainers, singers, bands, comedians, and dramatic actors. Tapes of these programs are still available. Books, too, can be heard on tape, many of which can be checked out from your local library.

Another commonplace source of potentially soothing auditory stimulation is the telephone. It can be pleasant to call a close friend or a long-distance relative with whom you have not spoken for a while.

Your childhood holds clues to calm your auditory senses. When you were little, it is likely that you associated certain sounds with peacefulness and pleasure. It may have been radio programs (late night baseball games you heard from the dark solitude of your bedroom) or television (the grace and delivery of a talented singer performing your favorite song).

Maybe you are soothed by the sounds of your mother cooking in the kitchen on Christmas Day or pleased by the excited noise of friends joining you for your birthday. A dog barking in the distance can bring back pleasant memories. Even mechanical noises like a lawn sprinkler rhythmically turning or the musical tones of an ice cream truck can provide the childhood link. Seek out these sounds. Listen for them. And then try to remember and reproduce the sounds in your head so that you are in charge.

Sense of Smell

The sense of smell is a conveyer of sensory stimulation that is quite basic on the evolutionary scale. Scents and smells around us instantly affect our feelings. Often in the reasonable attempt to make our environment clean and sterile, to avoid illness, we forget the power of wonderful odors.

Each of us knows the delight of walking into a kitchen where our favorite dish is being prepared. We all know how wonderful it feels to smell rich leather or freshly chopped wood. The smell of newly mown grass, the whiff of ocean spray are universal pleasures.

We also like the smell of colognes and perfumes. Nor should we forget the familiar, comforting smells of a newly washed sweater and an old reliable work shirt. There are more personal smells as well that bring a smile of recognition and a calming pause.

There are many ways to collect these smells. A fresh bowl of fruit or flowers on the dining room table can be both a visual and an olfactory pleasure. You may want to burn incense or brew fresh coffee or walk over to a friend's herb garden. In fact, you can control the intensity and "flavor" of smells by purchasing any number of sprays that mist your favorite odors into the air.

Again, it is helpful to think over your memories and

try to remember what smells pleased and delighted you over the years. Was it a trip to grandma's house? A ride in the countryside? How about a visit to the zoo? Childhood, that reservoir of naive charm and delight, will once more provide the answers. So program your nose.

Taste

For this sense, we have the help of every food advertisement on television or on billboards. Try to think of all the foods that are pleasing to you. It may not be as many as you first thought. Taste receptors on the tongue help to determine your subjective impressions.

What we want, however, is for the sense of taste to be tied to delicious memories of food and meals you enjoy.

Rebecca Steinberg knows exactly when a meal will perk up her spirits. And she has help in its preparation.

"My husband likes to cook. And my favorite evening, if I'm really tired or depressed, is for him to fix some wonderful gourmet dinner, finish it off with a chocolate dessert, and then watch an old movie on the VCR, stretched out on the sofa, being almost mindless.

"That's my idea of a good time. I guess that's everybody's idea of a good time."

Touch

With our sense of touch we appreciate all the lovely things around us that feel so good. Some have a preference for materials that are soft, fuzzy and plush. Others seek out smooth, hard, clean surfaces like marble, fine wood, or shiny metals. The touch of skin can be particularly satisfying. You can massage creams into your skin while listening to music or closing your eyes in reverie.

Sexual pleasures usually include many senses but are most heavily weighted toward touch. Caresses and kisses are ways that two people have of pleasing each other.

As with the sense of smell, you may wish to have items around the house that feel good: a velvet pillow, a smooth piece of wood that you found on the beach, worn marbles reminiscent of childhood pleasures. Put them close by, where they can be easily touched as you pass from, say, the living room to the kitchen. Sometimes, even the everyday routines of taking care of your body can hold special importance.

"You have to have a doctor's order to shampoo your hair in the hospital," says Sandra McCollum. "When I come off the ventilator there are three things I want to do. One is call my husband, one is wash my hair, and one is shave my legs—usually in that order.

"The doctors thought I was silly. You know, you can wait until tomorrow to wash your hair. They didn't understand that this was something that I had been lying there thinking about for three days. That this is the reward I'm going to give myself. And it doesn't take a lot of energy because the nurses are willing to help.

"The nurses generally were pleased because they realized that if I was fighting, I was probably going to make it."

You should also treat your body to a special experience, like a massage. You might want to get a foot massage or have somebody scratch your back. Sexual activity affords the most elegant and complex source of tactile pleasure, involving many areas of the body.

Kinesthetic Pleasure

Turn around. Open your mouth. Raise your left arm. The kinesthetic sense includes all the things you experience when you move your body. Walking. Skipping. Running. Jogging. Skiing. Swimming. Also to be considered are stretching, tensing, and relaxing your muscles. Sports and dancing are obvious sources of kinesthetic pleasure. They can be very complex or relatively simple. Some require practice and balance; others are less complicated.

For Mary Alice Kerr, horseback riding gives her the opportunity to be outdoors, in motion, and "freedom to leave the wheelchair behind." With a body that is slowly atrophying from multiple sclerosis, Mary Alice savors the visual and kinesthetic sensations of her legs against the movement of the horse. She has found a stable equipped with a ramp so she can mount from a wheelchair. The horses respond to voice and hand commands.

"Part of it," she says, "is that sensation of walking. You're more in control of where you're going. You turn the horse where you want to turn. The other thing is, I can watch my legs flex. I wear shorts. The horse is moving, your leg is moving, you can see your muscles flexing. So it's good exercise, too."

She and a friend were able to reach a place that was otherwise inaccessible, where they had a picnic lunch. Mary Alice transferred from the horse's back to the picnic table.

"I can get to places I couldn't get to, impossible to get to, without riding a horse. It gives you mobility you've lost."

Some are insistent in the exercise of their independence, to the point of accepting discomfort in order to affirm their vitality.

"I don't take painkillers," says Dorothy McCormick, who has almost constant pain in her right knee, "because I feel I might become desensitized to other pleasures as well."

"There is stress release from athletic activities," says Peter Clifton. "The concentration on the activity, your breathing, your stroke, your rhythm. Your other problems are put into perspective. I like being real big. I would prefer standing up, but I kind of like being real strong. You can't have a good mental attitude unless your body feels good."

Chapter Exercise

Check Your Senses

The following is a checklist of sensory activities. Check off those that you can associate with a childhood pleasure or a happy memory. Think of ways you might be able to re-experience that previously pleasurable sensation.

Sights

candles

crowds

mirrors

moon

handsome men

color

photos

pretty clothes

luxury autos

pretty women

Sounds

music

voices

crickets

fizz of open can of soda

tuned auto engine

rain

cat purring

ice cubes in glass

children playing in
the distance

Smells

food

flowers

gasoline

cut grass

leather

fresh paint

clean sheets

air after rainfall

sweat

Tastes

chocolate

wine

licorice

garlic

pizza

Tootsie Roll

peanut butter and jelly

lobster

maple syrup

Touch
velvet
wood
football
kiss
sunlight
massage
clay
warm wool sweater
spouse's/companion's arm around you

Kinesthetic
walking
stretching
sex
carnival ride
fishing
riding a bike
T'ai Chi
sitting quietly
airplane ride

This body is my house—it is not I:
Triumphant in this faith I live and die.
Frederic Lawrence Knowles

This chapter deals with four major issues that directly concern your body. Each is crucial to good health and emotional well-being. They are important enough to be the core issue of several books, not just brief parts of a chapter. Because their psychological impact is great for those with a chronic illness, they need to at least be touched upon in this context.

"I have always attempted to be responsible about my body without *kvetching* all the time," says Frances Smithson, a 70-year-old woman with scoliosis, cancer, and diabetes. "I pay attention to my body without specializing in it."

Let us look at food, medication, sex, and exercise.

Food

Think about the role of food in your life and how it relates to the level of pleasure and control of your physical state. This may seem like an offhand issue, one that was only important when you were little and your parents nagged you about eating wholesome meals. Chronic illness, as we have emphasized, evokes many childhood issues, and this is another one.

We take food into the body several times a day. It is usually an integral part of our daily schedule. We pick food to ease hungry feelings, to please our taste buds, to satisfy our nutritional needs, and to fit into the setting where we are getting the food. In relatively rapid fashion, our mind selects what it will take from the world around to become part of us. We may decide to eat fairly quickly. At some times, we deliberate about our food selection. Whatever the circumstance, there are many complicated, unconscious factors that affect our choice.

Carol Borneo, diagnosed with cancer, took advantage of that understanding in the context of special food requirements.

"If you are going to diet, you must do it slowly," she advises. "Tell your body why you are doing it and how long you will do it. I think the cells can understand. Keep talking."

Eating can be subsumed under two broad categories: nutrition and the "fine art of dining." The field of nutrition has good directives on what is necessary to keep your body working well. After assessing variables like height, age, and medical status, your doctor can tell you what your ideal weight range should be and what is needed to maintain it.

You already have a sense of that range. For many of us, it is a marginal weight, one at which we feel better than at other weights. Your doctor will tell you about the vitamins and minerals that should be part of your diet and may have you talk to a nutritionist to plan your meals. Issues such as water intake, alcohol, smoking, and caffeine may also be part of the picture.

These suggestions ideally should be the main impetus to guide you in choosing what you need to eat. It all sounds simple, but it is not. Impulsivity, personality, family habits, stress, and apathy all make a relatively simple process complex. This becomes more serious and complicated for the person with a chronic illness. Food frequently is an outlet for frustration and aggression. Often, depression and inactivity can lead people to neglect their nutritional needs.

Your doctor can tell you what is best for your body, but you are the only one who can follow through on the program. Eating the right foods can be as important as taking the right medicine. We often find that people who neglect or abuse good food habits do the same in other areas of their lives. What we want to make clear is that this is a realm of functioning, often overlooked, that you need to think about carefully.

Take time to consider the basics.

Let's look at the "fine art of dining." There are five questions for you to consider: Who? What? When? Where?

Why?

Food can be stuffed in one's mouth or it can be eaten with care and sensitivity. But the rule, here as elsewhere, should be: The more pleasure you allow yourself from any life function, the better. The way you plan to eat can make your day much more enjoyable than it may be now. The processes of shopping and cooking can be arts in and of themselves.

Certainly, you should think of the five Ws as a way to make eating a "class act."

Who

Plan to eat with good company—companionable friends, family, or even inanimate company (music, reading material, TV). Be sure that you are surrounded by something positive.

What
Think about flavors, aromatics, and types of food. Each meal should involve some planning. At home, have your favorite foods on hand. Try some new recipes. Search out ethnic foods with ingredients you are allowed to have.

When
It is probably not wise to eat your meals at random times. This does not keep you in control. If you eat at the same general time every day, you will have the pleasure of looking forward to each meal as well as the joy of taking in the food.

Where
Do you eat your meals in a pleasant environment? You are in charge of where you sit to eat. There is no one correct way to do this. If it pleases you to pick up food in a drive-through restaurant and eat in your car, that too can be pleasant. The question is, do *you* choose it?

Why
Think about what you want to happen when you eat. Is the meal just to take care of your hunger? Is it a time to catch up on gossip with friends? Is it a rare chance to stop and relax? Does it mark a special point in your day?

Sex

Millie Pappas is a bright 32-year-old sales clerk in a fashionable suburban clothing store. She is single and has a yet-undiagnosed pain on the right side of her body. She has had several exploratory surgeries, but the problem still interferes with her ability to walk easily. The disfiguring surgeries and the noticeable limp, though not always present, have made her self-conscious. Her friends have told her they hardly notice any physical problems.

On a recent Saturday night, Millie spent the evening with some acquaintances at a local restaurant. While there, she was introduced to a man who, it turns out, works just a few blocks from where she is employed. Now, a week or so later, she still cannot get him out of her mind.

Millie uses large parts of her day fantasizing about spending time with him. She imagines accidentally running in to him at lunchtime. She envisions conversations, laughter, after-dinner wine, and, perhaps, a first kiss. She has been playing variations of this scenario on almost a daily basis.

One evening, getting ready for bed, and fantasizing once again about being physically close to him, she goes into the bathroom and turns on the light. She is faced with the full-length mirror that she had bought expressly for the purpose of being able to see herself completely. She notes the effects of her illness on her entire body.

She becomes terribly saddened. The scars and rearranged flesh around the area of her hip seem especially unsightly tonight. She tries to cover the area with a towel, but this only makes her more self-conscious. The edge of the towel touches one of the chronic sore spots on her side. The stiffness seems to cruelly mock her fantasy.

She steps back a bit from the mirror and tries to look objectively at her whole person. All she can think of is her hip and how she looks. And, how she feels. No one, she is sure, could possibly want anyone who is deformed. Without warning, her romantic thoughts of a moment ago turn cold and stale.

The disability in this example is not severe, but it is chronic. As it does for others in a similar position, it stays at the edge of consciousness. Any disability throws off our sense of feeling comfortable and whole. When the physical problem is permanent or erratic, the personal impact takes an even greater toll.

Physical intimacy and lovemaking, the exchange of touches between two people, are highly nourishing sources of positive experience. The person with a physical problem often experiences, as Millie did, feelings of shame, self-consciousness, awkwardness, and a disturbed self-image. These can lead to performance anxiety, suppression of erotic fantasies, avoidance of sexual behavior, and negative feelings (usually angry), which block sexual feeling.

Often, problems that arise during an illness have their roots in early childhood issues. Sometimes, we find unresolved anger, fear of intimacy, and anxiety about commitment. This context is ideal for breeding poor communication. It can lead to a break in the natural, intimate sharing that is part of the relationship. Or, in Millie's case, it can prevent a relationship from even starting.

It also results in frustration and self-consciousness

in your spouse or lover because your companion doesn't know what to do, either. This does not mean the relationship will end, but it does mean that some part of the lifeline that connects two people has been knotted and injured.

The solution is one that sounds easy but is really quite complex. It involves the functioning of self-awareness and communication. Both require determination because, as usual, denial feels more familiar and comfortable.

Once you have worked through these issues, lovemaking can return. Your body will cooperate if you become a little innovative. There are solutions for sexual problems. Many of them, as you might well imagine, have been around for a long, long time.

There are three possible routes for solving these problems:

1. *Self-awareness.* Having just read this section may be sufficient to get you on your way to changing your situation. Insight and knowledge, and the courage to use them, are powerful resources for solving problems.

2. *Communicating with your partner.* This involves taking a risk, regardless of the length of your relationship, and expressing your deepest concerns.

3. *Using a counselor or psychology resources.* If it appears that the problem is not beginning to resolve, it may be time to seek professional help. The therapist can help you sort out what aspects of the problem are simple and acute

and which ones require more talking through and exploration of the finer details of the relationship.

Sexual functioning has great potential as a source of pleasure and intimacy. The pleasure can be intruded upon by chronic physical problems. Insight and communication can eliminate the intrusion, and pleasure in its fullest sense can return.

"So much of the healing process, in beginning and learning how to cope, is finding that a woman can still fall in love with you—which is pretty fun," asserts Peter Clifton. "It could be a real surprise sometimes."

Medication—The Double Whammy

Sometimes the medicine works and sometimes it doesn't. It is easy to imagine someone taking prescription medication, not getting the benefits expected, and just changing the medicine regime. This is not a good idea. The reason is not that your doctor is always right. The reason is that everybody is different, and often doctor and patient have to stop and discuss how each medication works.

Your doctor is not your parent. The relationship is not one of an absolute authority figure who rules over a child. Instead, it helps to think of your doctor as a paid medical advisor with good experience. You are the one who cares passionately about your health, and is totally committed to it.

When you get a prescription, follow the guidelines to the best of your ability. Then report back as clearly as possible about the results. If necessary, work out a new regime with the doctor. If you get into the habit of following a regular medication schedule that is effective, you will be in greater control of your body. You will trust it more. And if you discuss all the confusing issues about the effects of the medication with the doctor, you will trust your doctor more. If the medicine works with evenness and predictability, you will trust the medicine more. Well-placed trust makes life, with or without an illness, more reasonable and less frightening.

You can use special props to track what happens with you and your medicine.

1. Every night, put the medication for the next day into a labeled paper cup. That way, you can track what you have taken and what you have not taken.

2. Be sure to ask your doctor what to do for each medication if you miss taking a pill. You will make a mistake once in a while. Do you double the next dosage, change schedule, or just skip it? Get that information.

3. Put a chart near your medicine cabinet to check off the dosage for each day. Write a note when you feel particularly good or bad. Remember: You will need to keep a pencil or pen nearby, or you will forget. Take that chart with you on your next visit to the doctor. Your doctor will appreciate your serious efforts to track the medication.

Several of the people we interviewed suggested still a

fourth way to help you keep track of your medication.

"When you go to the doctor, take someone with you," said Carol Borneo. "Take a tape recorder and ask for what you need or to have something explained again, if that's necessary."

Helen Baer agrees. "People forget what they hear. I've had friends accompany me to specialists."

Now let's consider one of the major drawbacks of medication—side effects. For example, a classic side effect of arthritis medication is stomach pain. Medication taken for your lungs can make you feel jittery and experience palpitations. Depression is a side effect of medication for blood pressure or heart rate problems.

You take medication to control your diabetes and you may find yourself becoming lethargic. Some medicines used for neurological problems cause some people to feel distracted and less alert. These are all double whammies. You have found that somehow you are exchanging one symptom for another!

Reactions to the same drug can vary from person to person. Just because you experience a side effect doesn't mean everyone else will. First, you should tell your doctor. Among other things, he will record it in your chart, where it may become part of other medical decisions he might have to make with you.

The next thing you may do is feel angry. Anger is a healthy reaction when you are frustrated or thwarted. Feel that anger; consider telling someone about it, find a place to scream, kick a football for 15 minutes, bang some pots and pans.

It is also okay to grieve. It is appropriate to acknowledge that it is sad and disappointing that everything you do for your illness is complicated and messy. Life is like that. Even the most idealized wishes (lots of money, beauty, fame), when realized, have their drawbacks. So does your medicine.

Finally, we encourage you to track both the side effects and the primary effects of your medication. The side effects are real and should be monitored. They are part of your medical picture now. But so are the benefits of your medication, and it should be taken regularly.

There are secondary benefits as well, as Helen Baer has discovered, despite the nausea and tiredness from chemotherapy.

"I had to learn to plan carefully. I had to have someone be with me to drive." She reduced her work schedule for more than four months and went to bed early. In addition, "I was regimented about diet. I ran a couple of miles a day. I let people treat me well and take me places."

Don't feel guilty about the anger and grief associated with reactions to medicine. You cannot make the double whammy disappear, but you can, and should, take it seriously. Treat it with personal and scientific respect.

Medication is a particularly troublesome area because it is a constant reminder of the need to be dependent on factors that are imposed, rather than chosen: doctors, pill-taking schedules, side effects, the chronic, no-end-in-sight character of the illness. It is also tangible evidence that regardless of how good you may feel, there remains a lurking presence that can make itself known at any moment. It is not surprising, then, that faced with medication requirements, many people resort to primitive patterns of defense carried over from childhood experience.

A useful exercise is to determine into which of the following patterns you have fallen at one time or another.

1. *Repression* — "Forgetting" that you had medicine to take—for example, planning a business trip or vacation without bringing along the necessary supplies.

2. *Projection* — Blaming others, such as family members, for distracting you (by getting you angry, upset, etc.) and making you so nervous that you could not find time or energy to take the medicine.

3. *Denial* — Having a full, symptom-free afternoon with friends and insisting you are cured and do not need medicine.

4. *Reaction formation* —Attempting some highly stressful and medically unadvised activity, thereby "proving" that medication is not necessary.

5. *Regression* — Becoming depressed and petulant around the times of the required medication, thereby evoking concern and interest from those around you who remind you to take the medicine.

Clearly, these styles of dealing with anxiety are not constructive. There is nothing fancy or especially difficult about recognizing them. Whenever a problem about taking medicine surfaces, review this list and try to determine what is going on. Put a check mark next to the appropriate pattern. If you find that you have entered three or four marks over several months, it would probably be a good idea to discuss it with your doctor. Maybe some adjustments to dosage, explanation, timing, or method of taking the medications are in order.

Exercise

While preparing this book, we heard a great deal about exercise. The stories told by those we have interviewed sound like material used for magazine articles entitled "How I Changed My Life." They report that exercise has coincided with great changes in overall functioning, their self-esteem, and their view of their illness.

A surprising number have taken up skiing or continued with the sport. Not only does skiing bring pleasure to the kinesthetic senses, but it also connects you to the outdoors in a way that some other sports do not. As they become more involved in the activity, a sense of proportion takes hold. The connection between the physical and the mental becomes clearer. Somehow, the disability is more integrated into the whole.

There is an interesting phenomenon at work here. It is possible that one experience common to all people with a chronic disability is a sense of alienation from their bodies. We know that often people who are not struggling with a physical problem report the same difficulty. An illness or disability, however, definitely intensifies the experience.

Patients report that they feel somewhat detached from their physical being. They liken it to being an air traffic controller at a large terminal, where they are continually assessing their limbs, their stomach, their pain. Perhaps this is a stance that is necessary to help deal with the extent to which their body has failed them. The result is that gradually they lose touch with their bodily feelings, and a strange, surreal effect develops.

But when those we interviewed begin to exercise, something starts to flip around. Each stretch or tug at their muscles is a reminder that they still have a real live body—and that it works. It has the ability to feel, to be controlled, pushed, tensed, used well, and relaxed.

They find that they had forgotten the joy of moving through space of their own accord, by foot, by skis, by horseback, or even by navigating a wheelchair manually. They find that their withered muscles revive. They experience a new sense of competition in which they try to push and cheer themselves on, all for a physical goal that seemed irrelevant six months ago and impossible to accomplish one month earlier.

They come closer to their natural sense of self, certainly a worthwhile objective. A strong theme in these pages has been the benefits of trying something new. Here is that message again. There is no reason to remain intimidated. The older and wiser we become, the clearer it is that all success has followed struggle. Persistence seems to be one of the qualities that separates those who do from those who do not.

"Skiing—that is such a thrill," exults Peter Clifton. "The feeling of accomplishment. I've worked real hard at it for three years, and now I can ski as good as 90 percent of the people on the slopes. It's a real treat. It's just great when people see me come flying down the slope.

"That whole athletic premise that goes into just you and your body, it becomes a catharsis. It's truly something."

Look at some of the more objective or external benefits from exercise, whether gained from the great outdoors or a regulated routine with equipment at home or a health spa.

Physical
- Increase energy and stamina
- Increase muscle strength
- Improve flexibility
- Reduce muscle atrophy and bone loss

Health Benefits
- Reduce body fat, increase muscle
- Strengthen heart and improve circulation
- Relieve tension and stress
- Reduce lower back pain
- Reduce risk of heat disease
- Reduce cholesterol levels
- Slow down the aging process
- Reduce and even reverse effects of osteoporosis

Performance Benefits
- Work harder without becoming fatigued
- Sharpen skills for sports and recreation
- Increase mental alertness and concentration
- Feel better about yourself, increase self-esteem and confidence

"I felt a general overall feeling of well-being," says Phil Peterson, 58, who swims 20 laps three times a week. "I don't really know if my arthritic knees got better, but I felt better."

Appearance Benefits

- Maintain proper body weight
- Improve body symmetry; redistribute weight
- Firm and tone muscles
- Become more youthful-looking

"I can get away with not looking sick, unless I'm really bad," says Sandra McCollum. "I've got machines at home and am very rigorous in my exercises, and so I don't sound sick a lot. I mean, I cough and all that, but I just don't make a habit of talking about it."

But beware. Choosing the right arrangement is important. For Andy Nordstrum, the ages of those in his cardiac exercise group only "stimulated more anger. I'm 38 not 67. This is unlike me. Someone 67 was running and I was just walking."

This summary is broad but it touches on some major issues. However, there are more subtle gains that come from exercise.

1. It gives you a chance to join others in an activity that can be shared, although you must also guard against its stirring up unwanted, counterproductive emotions.

2. It gives you a chance to release tension that normally accumulates during the day.

3. It gives you a chance to push your body and see what new things it can do. It enables you to see if you can create goals that are more challenging. It enables you to compete, on a safe level, with yourself.

4. It gives you a chance to have a special time just to do something for yourself. It is a healthy way to celebrate your often ignored and neglected body.

5. It gives you a chance to do something completely independently. That may be new and a bit frightening. Consider it.

Exercise "makes me feel good," says Rebecca Steinberg, explaining it helps her to feel in charge. "I'm taking this into my own hands. I'm actually doing this for my own health. I'm taking responsibility for my actions and it feels real good. I'm just not passively going along with the disease."

The choice of exercise is yours. Consult with your doctor. Speak to your friends. Take advantage of a trial membership at a spa or sports club. Who knows? There may be a strong and sturdy athlete hidden in your body right now.

The whole is greater than the sum of its parts.

The people we interviewed not only survived with wisdom and spirit, they went beyond survival to reach out in a variety of ways to help or connect with others. They gathered their remarkable strengths and rose above the illness. It's important to remember their successes.

Many of those we talked with spoke of strong powerful forces within themselves that enabled them to adapt and cope. Many are not sure where the energy for this effort comes from or how it operates. They simply know it's there.

They reported that in times of crisis, some sense of being centered and directed comes to the fore and helps them do things they did not think they were able to do.

We can attempt to categorize those experiences medically as bursts of adrenalin; psychologically as strong character structure; religiously as spiritual commitment; or cognitively as simple coping skills. However, when all is said and done, we really do not know what is operating. There seems to be a blend of passion for life and common sense that makes for just the right mixture.

Reason tells us that these survivors all must have something in common. We heard similar reports from cardiac patients, cystic fibrosis patients, people with multiple sclerosis, cancer, diabetes, arthritis, and other chronic physical problems.

We know these people come from dramatically different backgrounds and have shaped their lives whether living alone, married, divorced, with or without children, with or without extended families, and from a range of age groups. They have degrees of disability that vary from episodic to constant.

Some had profound parental models from whom they learned how to cope; others did not. Some are from dysfunctional families. Are there any threads that connect them? There may be. Chronic illness puts the person with the illness into situations where common unpleasant experiences must be faced. These include:

1. Having important goals frustrated

2. Having doctors and medicine intrude on your privacy

3. Having anger towards medicine for not being able to fix you

4. Having the ability to look and feel normal disrupted

5. Having body concept distorted

6. Having simple work and leisure plans thwarted

7. Having fears about being partially or totally helpless

8. Having fears about death and suffering

9. Having times of loneliness because people don't or won't understand

10. Having feelings of humiliation in public places

11. Having angry feelings toward your loved ones because of your or their dilemma

12. Having angry feelings toward yourself for being vulnerable

13. Having a sense of disappointment about the unavailability of dreams that won't come true

14. Having trouble communicating

15. Having a sense of lost hope

16. Having depression because of that loss

17. Having cynicism about a culture that is not supportive

18. Having a sense that your suffering has been unfair

This is a long and depressing list. It is unlikely, however, that many people with chronic illness will disagree with the entirety of it. You will probably have from 5 to 10 more items yourself to add to make it more complete.

Despite this catalogue of universal woes, we still find that those we interviewed report a sense of energy and potency as they survey the path of their survival. This chapter was not part of the original outline for this book. But it had to be written because so many of those we spoke with kept referring to, by a variety of names, their surprising inner strength.

Each seemed to be internally stating, "I will not be overcome." They learned new skills and relearned old ones. They risked over and over to try new things. They worked at their recovery and accepted it, many with some impatience, as a day-to-day challenge. They shared their knowledge with others. They are feisty models of high drive and persistence. They each tipped the scales of fate and flipped them around.

• The learning-disabled student who in spite of his disability opens a successful hair-styling business and goes back to teach learning-disabled children how to persist.

• The chronically disabled woman with faulty lungs who repeatedly rises from the respirator to return to her life as wife and teacher of medical students dealing with frightening illnesses.

• The amputee who recovers from his loss and becomes a competitive skier and swimmer who teaches others how to succeed.

• The doctor with a liver transplant who continues his career using what he has experienced to make him more compassionate and understanding of his patients.

• The young girl who persists in her athletic endeavors despite the limits placed on her by her asthma and becomes a valuable team member.

We can see—indeed we can feel—the fortitude they have demonstrated reconquering their bodies and their minds. We say *re*conquering because that is a task already mastered in childhood. They have used their indomitable spirit to overrule the cosmic joke played on their unsuspecting bodies.

This book is about that process. They have worked, fumbled, persevered, and conquered. They kept at it. They keep at it. They have described for us the skills they have that are classic models for good adaptation. These are patience, courage, compassion, humor, risk taking, self-control, curiosity, loving, working, creativity, sympathy, flexibility, communication skills, self-reliance, and foresight. It is a totality of character and indomitability that is far greater than the individual parts.

Through the pages of this book, they have passed the baton to you. Take it and move on.

* * * * *

"I want a life free of diseases. I can't believe that if all the brilliant scientists worked on it, it would not be taken care of."

Carol Borneo

It was to Carol Borneo that Marcia Landau drove her car that cold November night in Albuquerque. Two months later, Carol Borneo died of widespread cancer.

37 Quick Pick-Me-Ups from Contributors to This Volume

Short-term goals are a lot safer than long-term goals.

It's nice to have help, but there's a difference between having help and having someone take over.

It's hard to describe exactly how you're still the same person when in so many ways you're different.

I really do want to know. I don't want bullshit.

There is no end to the rainbow. I could improve the odds, but that was all.

There is no one way. There is only your way.

There is so much in our society today that says, "Have a positive attitude." No. I have cancer, thank you. I get to feel bad. You go have a positive attitude.

People don't want to be around people who are miserable. I know I don't want to be around people who are miserable.

Warmth begets warmth. If someone smiles at you, smile back.

You have to be able to giggle. If you can giggle, others will join in and you can all come up with some really great things to giggle about. Search for giggles.

I learned that not being athlete of the year, girls still liked me anyway.

Why can't the pain be spread out? There are bad people in the world. Why can't they have the pain?

Pain makes me not be as frivolous as I used to be. It sharpens my focus.

I really, really enjoy working with children. It's a concentrated thing. When I'm so wrapped up in it, nothing can overcome that joy.

Never trust anybody who buys one pair of shoes.

Never trust anybody with feet the same size.

Because I was born different, I don't know how to play out some kind of thing to make myself special. I was special when I emerged.

You don't have to be cured to live healthy.

It's okay to get tired.

Taking charge of your disease leads to a healthy life, to a transformation from being controlled by illness to being in control.

I can't emphasize short-term goals enough. And the feeling of being triumphant when you've done that one little thing.

It's okay to be depressed if there's a reason to be depressed.

I've never taken myself real seriously; but I certainly have taken trying to stay alive seriously.

It makes you feel really good when you're beating the odds. And that's what I'm doing—beating the odds.

I always tell people: Don't be passive. Let everybody know you're there. Don't let them mistreat you.

I laugh at myself when I hurt myself. I laugh with my friends about it. It's mainly all you can do.

Figure out how to restructure your life so that the things you're doing now are important. Have something going on so you will have something to hold on to.

Nobody can predict a surprise.

Short-term goals are so important. You can say to yourself, "The most important thing for me to do right now is to eat my lunch. This is what I have to do now."

I have a disease; it is not who I am.

It may not be as tough as you thought it would be. In every instance, it was not as tough as I thought it would be .

Put your mind in the positive and take it one day at a time. They're crazy if they think it's my fault.

Life is transitory. You need to be ready to pick up your ego.

People say, "I don't want to feel sorry for myself," I say, "Why not? It's appropriate." The question is, how long does it last?

I don't view myself as a sick person. I think of myself as a healthy person who on occasion gets sick.

When you have nothing to lose, you've lived a life of nothing.

Often, it's the little things that count. Here are some easy-effort suggestions for reciprocal caring that don't quite fit into any one category. At one time, we all took them for granted.

Take a walk together.
Send a greeting card.
Clip and send a newspaper or magazine article of special interest.
Give a cookie.
Open a door.
Remember a birthday.
Bring over a little present for no occasion at all.
Offer a package of Life Savers.
Help run an errand.
Bring flowers.
Offer to give a back rub.
Phone just to see how someone is doing.
Carry something (to the car, from the mailbox, etc.).
Help put on a jacket.
Check to see how family members are doing.
Make a cup of tea.
Make sure to say hello and goodbye.
Tell someone about a TV program of interest.
Help someone to sit down.
Share a tape or record.
Bring someone a plant.
Lend or recommend a book to someone.
Take a photo and send a copy.
Be a pen pal (even with someone on the same block).

The titles of some of the selected readings are illness-specific. As suggested throughout this book, however, readers can gain from knowing about the problems of sufferers with illnesses other than their own. With this in mind, every book listed contains information that is potentially of value to all readers.

Chapter 2. Illness Alienates
- *Illness As a Metaphor*, by Susan Sontag (Vintage Books, 1979).
- *At a Journal Workshop* by Ira Progoff (Dialogue House Library, 1975)

Chapter 3. Riding the Cycles
- "Psychosocial aspects of chronic illness," in *Psychological Aspects of Serious Illness*, edited by Paul T. Costa, Jr., and Gary R. VandenBos (American Psychological Association, 1990)
- *Chronic Pain: America's Hidden Epidemic*, edited by Steven F. Brena (Atheneum/SMI, 1978)

Chapter 4. Monitoring Symptoms
- *Coping with Chronic Pain: A Patient's Guide to Wellness* by David Florence and Frank Hegedes (Sister Kenny Institute, 1982)
- *Peace, Love, and Healing: Bodymind Communication and the Path to Self-Healing—An Exploration* by Bernie S. Siegel (Harper & Row, 1989)
- *How to Cope with Illness* by Miriam Siegler and Humphry Osmond (Collier Books, 1979)

Chapter 5: Preparing for Battle
- *The 36-Hour Day* by Nancy Mace and Peter Robbins (Johns Hopkins University Press, 1981)
- *Coping with Kidney Failure: A Guide to Living with Kidney Failure for You and Your Family* by R. H. Phillips (Avery Publishing Group, 1987)
- *The Household Environment and Chronic Illness: Guidelines for Constructing and Maintaining a Less Polluted Residence* by G. Pfeiffer and C. Nikel (C. C. Thomas, 1980)

Chapter 6. One Step at a Time
- *Yes You Can: A Help Book for the Physically Disabled* by Helynn Hoffa and Gary Morgan (Pharos Books, 1990)
- *Aging with a Disability* by Roberta Trieschmann (Demos Publications, 1987)

Chapter 7: The Space That Heals
- *Solitude* by Anthony Storr (The Free Press, 1988)

Chapter 8: Try Something New
- *Arthritis: A Comprehensive Guide to Understanding Your Arthritis* (3rd edition), by James F. Fries (Addison Wesley, 1990)
- *The Arthritis Helpbook: A Tested Self-Management Program for Coping with Your Arthritis* (3rd edition), by Kate Lorig and James F. Fries (Addison-Wesley, 1990)
- *Toward a Psychology of Being* by Abraham H. Maslow (Van Nostrand, 1968)

Chapter 9. Don't Forget Your Daily Shots ... of Inspiration
- *Coping with Cancer* by Avery D. Weisman (McGraw-Hill, 1979)
- *Never Too Late* by John Holt (Merloyd-Lawrence Books, 1978)
- *To a Dancing God* by Sam Keen (Harper & Row, 1970)

Chapter 10: Well-Meaning Advice —Says Who?
- *Coping with Chronic Illness: Overcoming Powerlessness* by J. Miller (Davis Co., 1982)

Chapter 11. You Be the Judge
- *Anatomy of an Illness as Perceived by the Patient: Reflections on Healing and Regeneration* by Norman Cousins (Bantam Books, 1979)

Chapter 12: Laughing Out Loud
- Mark Twain, Erma Bombeck, James Thurber, Art Buchwald, the Marx Brothers

Chapter 13. Childhood Illnesses: Helping Your Child Cope

- *Children with Diabetes* by Linda M. Siminerio and Jean Betschart (American Diabetes Association, 1986)
- Chapter 13 in *Coping with Physical Illness* edited by Rudolf H. Moos (Plenum, 1979)
- *Luke Has Asthma, Too* (ages 3-7) by Alison Rogers (Waterfront Books, 1989)
- *Whole Parent / Whole Child: A Parent's Guide to Raising a Child with a Chronic Illness,* by Patricia M. Moynihan and Broatch Haig (DCI Publishing, 1990)

Chapter 14. If You Have Just Been Diagnosed

- *Coping with Crisis and Handicap* edited by Aubrey Milunsky (Plenum, 1981)
- *Diabetes: Caring for Your Emotions as Well as Your Health* by Jerry Edelwich and Archie Brodsky (Addison-Wesley, 1986)
- *On Death and Dying* by Elisabeth Kubler-Ross (MacMillan, 1969)

Chapter 15: When to Say "Ouch"

- *We Are Not Alone: Learning to Live with Chronic Illness* by Sefra Kobrin Pitzele (Thompson and Company, 1985)

Chapter 16. Mutual Caring

- *The Healing Family* by Stephanie Simonton (Bantam Books, 1984)
- *Heartsearch: Toward Healing Lupus* by Donna Hamil Talman (North Atlantic Books, 1991)
- *Mainstay: For the Well Spouse of the Chronically Ill* by Maggie Strong (Little Brown, 1988)
- *The Dance of Anger* by Harriet Lerner (Harper Row, 1985)

Chapter 17: Feelings and Communication

- *Building a New Dream: Family Guide to Coping with Chronic Illness and Disability* by Janet Maurer and Patricia D. Strasberg (Addison-Wesley, 1989)

- *Living Beyond Fear: A Course for Coping with the Emotional Aspects of Life-Threatening Illness* by Jeanne Segal (Ballantine Books, 1989)
- *Sailing* by Susan Kenney (Viking, 1988)
- *The Transparent Self* by Sidney Jourard (Van Nostrand Reinhold Co., 1964)

Chapter 18. Dazzle Your Senses
- *Sexual Sabotage: How to Enjoy Sex in Spite of Physical and Emotional Problems* by Sherwin A. Kaufman (MacMillan, 1981)

Chapter 19: Listening to Your Body
- *Diabetes* by Steven Tiger (J. Messner, 1987)
- *Transforming Body Image: Learning to Love the Body You Have* by Marcia Germaine Hutchinson (The Crossing Press, 1985)
- *Maximizing Your Health* edited by D. Frankel and P. Buxbaum (National Multiple Sclerosis Society, 1982)
- *The New Aerobics* by Kenneth Cooper (Bantam Books, 1970)

Chapter 20: Surviving with Wisdom and Spirit
- *Flying Without Wings* by Arnold R. Beisser (Doubleday, 1989)
- *Living With Chronic Illness: Days of Patience and Passion* by Cheri Register (The Free Press, 1987)
- *Necessary Losses* by Judith Viorst (Ballantine Books, 1986)

CHRONIMED Publishing Books of Related Interest

☐ **When You're Sick and Don't Know Why: Coping with Your Undiagnosed Illness** by Linda Hanner, John J. Witek, M.D., with Robert B. Clift, Ph.D. This warm and comprehensive guide offers hope and practical advice for dealing with an undiagnosed illness and for obtaining an accurate diagnosis as quickly as possible. "Reassuring, helpful, and broadly applicable." —Mary Hager, Newsweek
004087, ISBN 0-937721-83-2, $9.95

☐ **Diagnosing Your Doctor** by Arthur R. Pell, Ph.D. Authoritative, straightforward, and powerful, this book tells how to get the most from doctors and medical professionals—and shows you how to ask tough questions to get the right answers.
004090, ISBN 0-937721-87-5, $9.95

☐ **Minute Health Tips: Medical Advice and Facts at a Glance** byThomas Welch, M.D. This valuable and easy-to-use guide discusses routine health problems, offers preventive medicine tips, shows you how to make doctor visits more informational, and much more.
004088, ISBN 0-937721-85-9, $8.95

☐ **Doctor, Why Do I Hurt So Much?** by Mark H. Greenberg, M.D., Lucille Frank, M.D., & Jackson Braider. This revolutionary guide will show you how to find relief from symptoms of over 100 different types of arthritis (and dozens of other related illnesses) as well as the causes.
004091, ISBN 0-937721-88-3, $14.95

☐ **Emergency Medical Treatment: Infants— A Handbook of What to Do in an Emergency to Keep an Infant Alive Until Help Arrives** by Stephen Vogel, M.D., and David Manhoff, produced in cooperation with the National Safety Council. This easy-to-follow, step-by-step guide tells exactly what to do during the most common, life-threatening situations you might encounter for infants. Fully illustrated and indexed with thumb tabs.
004582, ISBN 0-916363-01-5, $7.95

☐ **Emergency Medical Treatment: Children— A Handbook of What to Do in an Emergency to Keep a Child Alive Until Help Arrives** by Stephen Vogel, M.D., and David Manhoff, produced in cooperation with the National Safety Council. This easy-to-follow, step-by-step guide tells exactly what to do during the most common, life-threatening situations you might encounter for children. Fully illustrated and indexed with thumb tabs.
004583, ISBN 0-916363-00-7, $7.95

☐ **Emergency Medical Treatment: Adults— A Handbook of What to Do in an Emergency to Keep an Adult Alive Until Help Arrives by** Stephen Vogel, M.D., and David Manhoff, produced in cooperation with the National Safety Council. This easy-to-follow, step-by-step guide tells exactly what to do during the most common, life-threatening situations you might encounter for adults. Fully illustrated and indexed with thumb tabs.
004584, ISBN 0-916363-05-8, $7.95

☐ **The Physician Within** by Catherine Feste. Here internationally renowned health motivation specialist, Cathy Feste, focuses on motivating those with a health challenge, and anyone else, to stay on their regimen and follow healthy behavior.
004019, ISBN 0-937721-19-0, $8.95

☐ **Whole Parent/Whole Child: A Parent's Guide to Raising a Child with a Chronic Illness** by Patricia Moynihan, R.N., P.N.P., M.P.H., and Broatch Haig, R.D., C.D.E. Everything parents of children with chronic health conditions need to know is here. With authority, insight, and compassion, this book shows you how to be the kind of parent you want to be and how to help your child lead the fullest life possible.
004051, ISBN 0-937721-53-0, $9.95

☐ **I Can Cope: Staying Healthy with Cancer** by Judi Johnson, R.N., Ph.D., and Linda Klein. This book is a clear, comprehensive resource for anyone whose life has been touched by cancer. And it's by Judi Johnson, co-founder of the American Cancer Society's internationally acclaimed "I Can Cope" program, which helps over 40,000 people a year.
004026, ISBN 0-937721-28-X, $8.95

☐ **Making the Most of Medicare: A Personal Guide Through the Medicare Maze** by Arthur R. Pell, Ph.D. Finally, a book that actually helps overcome the government red tape associated with Medicare. It shows what can and cannot be expected from Medicare and provides easily understood explanations of Medicare policies—plus tips on how to use them for optimum advantage.
004071, ISBN 0-937721-66-2, $11.95

☐ **Retirement: New Beginnings, New Challenges, New Successes** by Leo Hauser and Vincent Miller. From two internationally renowned motivational speakers, trainers, and retirees comes a book that will help you achieve new goals in retirement. It's a plan of action that charts a course to successful, rewarding, and active retirement.
004059, ISBN 0-937721-59-X, $5.95

☐ **Fast Food Facts** by Marion Franz, RD. This revised and up-to-date best-seller shows how to make smart nutritional choices at fast food restaurants—and tells what to avoid. Includes complete nutrition information on more than 1,000 menu offerings from the 32 largest fast food chains.
Standard-size edition   004068, ISBN 0-937721-67-0, $6.95
Pocket edition   004073, ISBN 0-937721-69-7, $4.95

☐ **Convenience Food Facts** by Arlene Monk, RD. Includes complete nutrition information, tips, and exchange values on over 1,500 popular name-brand processed foods commonly found in grocery store freezers and shelves. It helps you plan easy-to-prepare, nutritious meals.
004081, ISBN 0-937721-77-8, $10.95

☐ **All-American Low-Fat Meals in Minutes** by M.J. Smith, RD, LD, MA. Filled with tantalizing recipes and valuable tips, this cookbook makes great-tasting low-fat foods a snap for holidays, special occasions, or everyday. Most recipes take only minutes to prepare.
004079, ISBN 0-937721-73-5, $12.95

☐ **It's Your Body** by Paul Terry, Ph.D., and Allan Kind, M.D., F.A.C.P. Here are the latest facts on every facet of preventive medicine—from new ways of avoiding cancer to curbing risks during pregnancy. Complete with the newest guidelines from the American College of Physicians and the U.S. Preventive Services Task Force.
004203, ISBN 1-56561-007-5, $9.95

Buy them at your local bookstore or use this
convenient coupon for ordering.

CHRONIMED Publishing
P.O. Box 47945
Minneapolis, MN 55447-9727

Please send me the books I have checked above. I am enclosing $_____. (Please add $2.50 to this order to cover postage and handling. Minnesota residents add 6.5% sales tax.) Send check or money order, no cash or C.O.D.'s. Prices are subject to change without notice.

Name _____

Address _____

City _____ State _____ Zip _____

Allow 4 to 6 weeks for delivery.
Quantity discounts available upon request.

Or order by phone: 1-800-848-2793,
1-800-444-5951 (non-metro area of Minnesota)
612-541-0239 (Minneapolis/St. Paul metro area).

Please have your credit card number ready.